Regression Analysis

Analysis

AN INTUITIVE GUIDE FOR USING
AND INTERPRETING LINEAR MODELS

Jim Frost

Statistics By Jim Publishing

STATE COLLEGE, PENNSYLVANIA

U.S.A.

Published by: Statistics By Jim Publishing

To contact the author, please email: jim@statisticsbyjim.com.

Visit the author's website at statisticsbyjim.com.

Quantity sales. Special discounts are available on quantity purchases. For details, contact the email address above.

Regression Analysis: An Intuitive Guide for Using and Interpreting Linear Models / Jim Frost. —1st ed.

ISBN 978-1-7354311-8-5

Contents

i

To Carmen and Morgan who made this book possible through their encouragement and support.

The best thing about being a statistician is that you get to play in everyone's backyard.

–John Tukey

My Approach to Teaching Regression and Statistics

I love statistics and analyzing data! I also love talking and writing about it. I was a researcher at a major university. Then, I spent over a decade working at a major statistical software company. During my time at the statistical software company, I learned how to present statistics in a manner that makes it more intuitive. I want you to understand the essential concepts, practices, and knowledge for regression analysis so you can analyze your data confidently. That's the goal of my book.

In this book, you'll learn many facets of regression analysis including the following:

- How regression works and when to use it.
- Selecting the correct type of regression analysis.
- Specifying the best model.
- Interpreting the results.
- Assessing the fit of the model.

- Generating predictions and evaluating their precision.
- Checking the assumptions.
- Examples of different types of regression analyses.

I'll help you intuitively understand regression analysis by focusing on concepts and graphs rather than equations and formulas. I use regular, everyday language so you can grasp the fundamentals of regression analysis at a deeper level. I'll provide practical tips for performing your analysis. You will learn how to interpret the results while being confident that you're conducting the analysis correctly. You'll be able to trust your results because you'll know that you're performing regression properly and know how to detect and correct problems.

Regardless of your background, I will take you through how to perform regression analysis. Students, career changers, and even current analysts looking to take your skills to the next level, this book has absolutely everything you need to know for regression analysis.

I've literally received thousands of requests from aspiring data scientists for guidance in performing regression analysis. This book is my answer - years of knowledge and thousands of hours of hard work distilled into a thorough, practical guide for performing regression analysis.

You'll notice that there are not many equations in this book. After all, you should let your statistical software handle the calculations so you don't get bogged down in the calculations and can instead focus on understanding your results. Instead, I focus on the concepts and practices that you'll need to know to perform the analysis and interpret the results correctly. I'll use more graphs than equations!

Don't get me wrong. Equations are important. Equations are the framework that makes the magic, but the truly fascinating aspects are what it all means. I want you to learn the true essence of regression analysis. If you need the equations, you'll find them in most textbooks.

Please note that throughout this book I use Minitab statistical software. However, this book is not about teaching particular software but rather how to perform regression analysis. All common statistical software packages should be able to perform the analyses that I show. There is nothing in here that is unique to Minitab.

For the examples in this book, I use datasets that you can download for free from my website so you can learn by doing. To obtain these files, go to:

https://statisticsbyjim.com/regression_book

CHAPTER 1

Correlation and an Introduction to Regression

Before we tackle regression analysis, we need to understand correlation. In fact, I've described regression analysis as taking correlation to the next level! Many of the practices and concepts surrounding correlation also apply to regression analysis. It's also a simpler analysis that is a more familiar subject for many. Bear with me because the correlation topics in this section apply to regression analysis as well. It's a great place to start!

A correlation between variables indicates that as one variable changes in value, the other variable tends to change in a specific direction. Understanding that relationship is useful because we can use the value of one variable to predict the value of the other variable. For example, height and weight are correlated—as height increases, weight also tends to increase. Consequently, if we observe an individual who is unusually tall, we can predict that his weight is also above the average. In statistics, correlation is a quantitative assessment that measures both the direction and the strength of this tendency to vary together.

There are different types of correlation that you can use for different kinds of data. In this chapter, I cover the most common type of correlation—Pearson's correlation coefficient.

Before we get into the numbers, let's graph some data first so we can understand the concept behind what we are measuring.

Graph Your Data to Find Correlations

Scatterplots are a great way to check quickly for relationships between pairs of continuous data. The scatterplot below displays the height and weight of pre-teenage girls. Each dot on the graph represents an individual girl and her combination of height and weight. These data are real data that I collected during an experiment. We'll return to this dataset multiple times throughout this book. To follow along, use the CSV data file: HeightWeight.

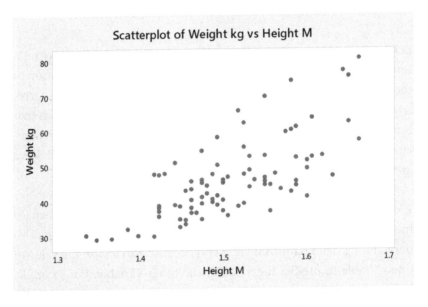

At a glance, you can see that there is a relationship between height and weight. As height increases, weight also tends to increase. However, it's not a perfect relationship. If you look at a specific height, say 1.5 meters, you can see that there is a range of weights associated with it.

You can also find short people who weigh more than taller people. However, the general tendency that height and weight increase together is unquestionably present.

Pearson's correlation takes all of the data points on this graph and represents them with a single summary statistic. In this case, the statistical output below indicates that the correlation is 0.705.

```
Correlation: Height M, Weight kg

Pearson correlation of Height M and Weight kg = 0.705
P-Value = 0.000
```

What do the correlation and p-value mean? We'll interpret the output soon. First, let's look at a range of possible correlation values so we can understand how our height and weight example fits in.

Interpret the Pearson's Correlation Coefficient

Pearson's correlation coefficient is represented by the Greek letter rho (ρ) for the population parameter and r for a sample statistic. This coefficient is a single number that measures both the strength and direction of the linear relationship between two continuous variables. Values can range from -1 to +1.

- **Strength:** The greater the absolute value of the coefficient, the stronger the relationship.
    - The extreme values of -1 and 1 indicate a perfectly linear relationship where a change in one variable is accompanied by a perfectly consistent change in the other. For these relationships, all of the data points fall on a line. In practice, you won't see either type of perfect relationship.
    - A coefficient of zero represents no linear relationship. As one variable increases, there is no tendency in the other variable to either increase or decrease.

- When the value is in-between 0 and +1/-1, there is a relationship, but the points don't all fall on a line. As r approaches -1 or 1, the strength of the relationship increases and the data points tend to fall closer to a line.
- **Direction:** The coefficient sign represents the direction of the relationship.
  - Positive coefficients indicate that when the value of one variable increases, the value of the other variable also tends to increase. Positive relationships produce an upward slope on a scatterplot.
  - Negative coefficients represent cases when the value of one variable increases, the value of the other variable tends to decrease. Negative relationships produce a downward slope.

Examples of Positive and Negative Correlations

An example of a positive correlation is the relationship between the speed of a wind turbine and the amount of energy it produces. As the turbine speed increases, electricity production also increases.

An example of a negative correlation is the relationship between outdoor temperature and heating costs. As the temperature increases, heating costs decrease.

Graphs for Different Correlations

Graphs always help bring concepts to life. The scatterplots represent a spectrum of different relationships. I've held the horizontal and vertical scales of the scatterplots constant to allow for valid comparisons between them.

Correlation = +1: A perfect positive relationship.

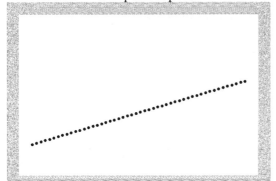

Correlation = 0.8: A fairly strong positive relationship.

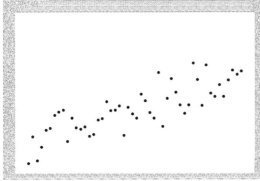

Correlation = 0.6: A moderate positive relationship.

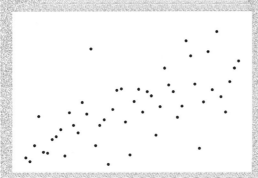

Correlation = 0: No relationship. As one value increases, there is no tendency for the other value to change in a specific direction.

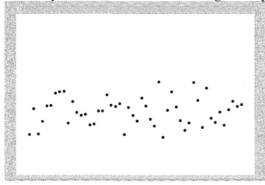

Correlation = -1: A perfect negative relationship.

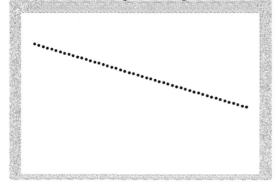

Correlation = -0.8: A fairly strong negative relationship.

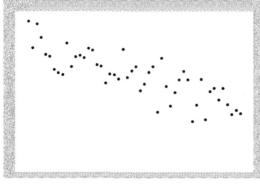

Correlation = -0.6: A moderate negative relationship.

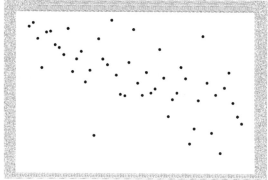

Discussion about the Correlation Scatterplots

For the previous scatterplots, I created one positive relationship between the variables and one negative relationship between the variables. Then, I varied only the amount of dispersion between the data points and the line that defines the relationship. That process illustrates how correlation measures the strength of the relationship. The stronger the relationship, the closer the data points fall to the line. I didn't include plots for weaker correlations that are closer to zero than 0.6 and -0.6 because they start to look like blobs of dots and it's hard to see the relationship.

A common misinterpretation is that a negative correlation coefficient indicates there is no relationship between a pair of variables. After all, a negative correlation sounds suspiciously like no relationship. However, the scatterplots for the negative correlations display real relationships. For negative relationships, high values of one variable are associated with low values of another variable. For example, there is a negative correlation between school absences and grades. As the number of absences increases, the grades decrease.

Earlier I mentioned how crucial it is to graph your data to understand them better. However, a quantitative assessment of the relationship does have an advantage. Graphs are a great way to visualize the data, but the scaling can exaggerate or weaken the appearance of a relationship. Additionally, the automatic scaling in most statistical software tends to make all data look similar.

Fortunately, Pearson's correlation coefficient is unaffected by scaling issues. Consequently, a statistical assessment is better for determining the precise strength of the relationship.

Graphs and the relevant statistical measures often work better in tandem.

Pearson's Correlation Measures Linear Relationships

Pearson's correlation measures only *linear* relationships. Consequently, if your data contain a curvilinear relationship, the correlation coefficient will not detect it. For example, the correlation for the data in the scatterplot below is zero. However, there is a relationship between the two variables—it's just not linear.

This example illustrates another reason to graph your data! Just because the coefficient is near zero, it doesn't necessarily indicate that there is no relationship.

Hypothesis Test for Correlations

Correlations have a hypothesis test. As with any hypothesis test, this test takes sample data and evaluates two mutually exclusive statements about the population from which the sample was drawn. For Pearson correlations, the two hypotheses are the following:

- **Null hypothesis**: There is no linear relationship between the two variables. $\rho = 0$.
- **Alternative hypothesis**: There is a linear relationship between the two variables. $\rho \neq 0$.

A correlation of zero indicates that no linear relationship exists. If your p-value is less than your significance level, the sample contains sufficient evidence to reject the null hypothesis and conclude that the correlation does not equal zero. In other words, the sample data support the notion that the relationship exists in the population.

Interpreting our Height and Weight Example

Now that we have seen a range of positive and negative relationships, let's see how our correlation of 0.705 fits in. We know that it's a positive relationship. As height increases, weight tends to increase. Regarding the strength of the relationship, the graph shows that it's not a very strong relationship where the data points tightly hug a line. However, it's not an entirely amorphous blob with a very low correlation. It's somewhere in between. That description matches our moderate correlation of 0.705.

For the hypothesis test, our p-value equals 0.000. This p-value is less than any reasonable significance level. Consequently, we can reject the null hypothesis and conclude that the relationship is statistically significant. The sample data provide sufficient evidence to conclude that the relationship between height and weight exists in the population of preteen girls.

Correlation Does Not Imply Causation

I'm sure you've heard this expression before, and it is a crucial warning. Correlation between two variables indicates that changes in one variable are associated with changes in the other variable. However, correlation does not mean that the changes in one variable actually *cause* the changes in the other variable.

Sometimes it is clear that there is a causal relationship. For the height and weight data, it makes sense that adding more vertical structure to a body *causes* the total mass to increase. Or, increasing the wattage of lightbulbs *causes* the light output to increase.

However, in other cases, a causal relationship is not possible. For example, ice cream sales and shark attacks are positively correlated. Clearly, selling more ice cream does not cause shark attacks (or vice versa). Instead, a third variable, outdoor temperatures, causes changes in the other two variables. Higher temperatures increase both sales of ice cream and the number of swimmers in the ocean, which creates the apparent relationship between ice cream sales and shark attacks.

In statistics, you typically need to perform a randomized, controlled experiment to determine that a relationship is causal rather than merely correlation.

How Strong of a Correlation is Considered Good?

What is a good correlation? How high should it be? These are commonly asked questions. I have seen several schemes that attempt to classify correlations as strong, medium, and weak.

However, there is only one correct answer. The correlation coefficient should accurately reflect the strength of the relationship. Take a look at the correlation between the height and weight data, 0.705. It's not a very strong relationship, but it accurately represents our data.

An accurate representation is the best-case scenario for using a statistic to describe an entire dataset.

The strength of any relationship naturally depends on the specific pair of variables. Some research questions involve weaker relationships than other subject areas. Case in point, humans are hard to predict. Studies that assess relationships involving human behavior tend to have correlations weaker than +/- 0.6.

However, if you analyze two variables in a physical process, and have very precise measurements, you might expect correlations near +1 or -1. There is no one-size fits all best answer for how strong a relationship should be. The correct correlation value depends on your study area. We run into this same issue in regression analysis.

Common Themes with Regression

Understanding correlation is a good place to start learning regression. In fact, there are several themes that I touch upon in this section that show up throughout this book.

For instance, analysts naturally want to fit models that explain more and more of the variability in the data. And, they come up with classification schemes for how well the model fits the data. However, there is a natural amount of variability that the model can't explain just as there was in the height and weight correlation example. Regression models can be forced to go past this natural boundary, but bad things happen. Throughout this book, be aware of the tension between trying to explain as much variability as possible and ensuring that you don't go too far. This issue pops up multiple times!

Additionally, for regression analysis, you'll need to use statistical measures in conjunction with graphs just like we did with correlation. This combination provides you the best understanding of your data and the analytical results.

Regression Takes Correlation to the Next Level

Wouldn't it be nice if instead of just describing the strength of the relationship between height and weight, we could define the relationship itself using an equation? Regression analysis does just that by finding the line and corresponding equation that provides the best fit to our dataset. We can use that equation to understand how much weight increases with each additional unit of height and to make predictions for specific heights.

Regression analysis allows us to expand on correlation in other ways. If we have more variables that explain changes in weight, we can include them in the model and potentially improve our predictions. And, if the relationship is curved, we can still fit a regression model to the data.

Additionally, a form of the Pearson correlation coefficient shows up in regression analysis. R-squared is a primary measure of how well a regression model fits the data. This statistic represents the percentage of variation in one variable that other variables explain. For a pair of variables, R-squared is simply the square of the Pearson's correlation coefficient. For example, squaring the height-weight correlation coefficient of 0.705 produces an R-squared of 0.497, or 49.7%. In other words, height explains about half the variability of weight in preteen girls.

But we're getting ahead of ourselves. I'll cover R-squared in much more detail in both chapters 2 and 6.

Fundamental Terms and Goals of Regression

The first questions you have are probably: When should I use regression analysis? And, why? Let's dig right into these questions! In this section, I explain the capabilities of regression analysis, the types of relationships it can assess, how it controls the variables, and generally why I love it! You'll learn when you should consider using regression analysis.

As a statistician, I should probably tell you that I love all statistical analyses equally—like parents with their kids. But, shhh, I have secret! Regression analysis is my favorite because it provides tremendous flexibility and it is useful in so many different circumstances.

You might run across unfamiliar terms. Don't worry. I'll cover all of them throughout this book! The upcoming section provides a preview for things you'll learn later in the book. For now, let's define several basics—the fundamental types of variables that you'll include in your regression analysis and your primary goals for using regression analysis.

Dependent Variables

The dependent variable is a variable that you want to explain or predict using the model. The values of this variable *depend* on other variables. It's also known as the response variable, outcome variable, and it is commonly denoted using a Y. Traditionally, analysts graph dependent variables on the vertical, or Y, axis.

Independent Variables

Independent variables are the variables that you include in the model to explain or predict changes in the dependent variable. In controlled experiments, researchers systematically set and change the values of the independent variables. However, in observational studies, values of the independent variables are not set by researchers but rather observed. These variables are also known as predictor variables, input variables, and are commonly denoted using Xs. On graphs, analysts place independent variables on the horizontal, or X, axis.

Simple versus Multiple Regression

When you include one independent variable in the model, you are performing simple regression. For more than one independent variable, it is multiple regression. Despite the different names, it's really the same analysis with the same interpretations and assumptions.

Goals of Regression Analysis

Regression analysis mathematically describes the relationships between independent variables and a dependent variable. Use regression for two primary goals:

- To understand the relationships between these variables. How do changes in the independent variables relate to changes in the dependent variable?
- To predict the dependent variable by entering values for the independent variables into the regression equation.

Example of a Regression Analysis

Suppose a researcher studies the relationship between wattage and the output from a light bulb. In this study, light output is the dependent variable because it depends on the wattage. Wattage is the independent variable.

After performing the regression analysis, the researcher will understand the nature of the relationship between these two variables. Is this relationship statistically significant? What effect does wattage have on light output? For a given wattage, how much light output does the model predict?

Specifically, the regression equation describes the relationship between wattage and light output. P-values indicate whether the relationship is statistically significant. And, the researcher can enter wattage values into the equation to predict light output.

Regression Analyzes a Wide Variety of Relationships

Use regression analysis to describe the relationships between a set of independent variables and the dependent variable. Regression analysis produces a regression equation where the coefficients represent the relationship between each independent variable and the dependent variable. You can also use the equation to make predictions.

Regression analysis can handle many things. For example, you can use regression analysis to do the following:

- Model multiple independent variables
- Include continuous and categorical variables
- Model linear and curvilinear relationships
- Assess interaction terms to determine whether the effect of one independent variable depends on the value of another variable

These capabilities are all cool, but they don't include an almost magical ability. Regression analysis can unscramble very intricate problems where the variables are entangled like spaghetti. For example, imagine you're a researcher studying any of the following:

- Do socio-economic status and race affect educational achievement?
- Do education and IQ affect earnings?
- Do exercise habits and diet effect weight?
- Are drinking coffee and smoking cigarettes related to mortality risk?
- Does a particular exercise intervention have an impact on bone density that is a distinct effect from other physical activities?

More on the last two examples later!

All these research questions have entwined independent variables that can influence the dependent variables. How do you untangle a web of related variables? Which variables are statistically significant and what role does each one play? Regression comes to the rescue because you can use it for all of these scenarios!

Using Regression to Control Independent Variables

As I mentioned, regression analysis describes how the changes in each independent variable are related to changes in the dependent variable. Crucially, regression also statistically controls every variable in your model.

What does controlling for a variable mean?

Typically, research studies need to isolate the role of each variable they are assessing. For example, I participated in an exercise intervention study where our goal was to determine whether the exercise intervention increased the subjects' bone mineral density. We needed to isolate the role of the exercise intervention from everything else that can impact bone mineral density, which ranges from diet to other physical activity.

Regression analysis does this by estimating the effect that changing one independent variable has on the dependent variable while holding all the other independent variables constant. This process allows you to understand the role of each independent variable without worrying about the other variables in the model. Again, you want to isolate the effect of each variable.

How do you control the other variables in regression?

A beautiful aspect of regression analysis is that you hold the other independent variables constant by merely including them in your model! Let's look at this in action with an example.

A recent study analyzed the effect of coffee consumption on mortality. The first results indicated that higher coffee intake is related to a higher risk of death. However, coffee drinkers frequently smoke, and the researchers did not include smoking in their initial model. After they included smoking in the model, the regression results indicated that coffee intake lowers the risk of mortality while smoking increases it. This model isolates the role of each variable while holding the other variable constant. You can assess the effect of coffee intake while controlling for smoking. Conveniently, you're also controlling for coffee intake when looking at the effect of smoking.

Note that the study also illustrates how excluding a relevant variable can produce misleading results. Omitting an important variable causes it to be uncontrolled, and it can bias the results for the variables that you do include in the model. In the previous example, the first model without smoking could not control for this important variable, which forced the model to include the effect of smoking in another variable (coffee consumption).

This warning is particularly applicable for observational studies where the effects of omitted variables might be unbalanced. On the other hand, the randomization process in a true experiment tends to distribute the effects of these variables equally, which lessens omitted variable bias. You'll learn about this form of bias in detail in chapter 7.

An Introduction to Regression Output

It's time to get our feet wet and interpret regression output. The best way to understand the value of regression analysis is to see an example. In Chapter 3, I cover all of these statistics in much greater detail. For now, you just need to understand the type of information that regression analysis provides.

P-values and coefficients are the key regression output. Collectively, these statistics indicate whether the variables are statistically significant and describe the relationships between the independent variables and the dependent variable.

Low p-values (typically < 0.05) indicate that the independent variable is statistically significant. Regression analysis is a form of inferential statistics. Consequently, the p-values help determine whether the relationships that you observe in your sample also exist in the larger population.

The coefficients for the independent variables represent the average change in the dependent variable given a one-unit change in the independent variable (IV) while controlling the other IVs.

For instance, if your dependent variable is income and your independent variables include IQ and education (among other relevant variables), you might see output like this:

```
Coefficients

Term           Coef  SE Coef         T      P
Constant    483.670  39.5671   12.2241  0.000
IQ            4.796   0.9511    5.0429  0.000
Education    24.215   1.9405   12.4785  0.000
```

The low p-values indicate that both education and IQ are statistically significant. The coefficient for IQ (4.796) indicates that each additional IQ point increases your income by an average of approximately $4.80 while controlling everything else in the model. Furthermore, the education coefficient (24.215) indicates that an additional year of education increases average earnings by $24.22 while holding the other variables constant.

Using regression analysis gives you the ability to separate the effects of complicated research questions. You can disentangle the spaghetti noodles by modeling and controlling all relevant variables, and then assess the role that each one plays.

We'll cover how to interpret regression analysis in much more detail in later chapters!

Review and Next Steps

In this chapter, we covered correlation between variables because it's such a good lead-in for regression. Correlation provides you with a look at some of the fundamental issues we'll address in regression analysis itself—different types of trends in the data and the variability around those trends.

Then, you learned about regression's fundamental goals, its capabilities, and why you'd use it for your study. You can use regression models to describe the relationship between each independent variable and the dependent variable. You can also enter values into the regression equation to predict the mean of the dependent variable. We even took a quick peek at some example regression output and interpreted it.

Finally, we saw how regression analysis controls, or holds constant, all the variables you include in the model. This feature allows you to isolate the role of each independent variable.

This chapter serves as an introduction to all the above. We'll revisit all these concepts throughout this book. Next, you'll learn how least squares regression fits the best line through a dataset.

CHAPTER 2

Regression Basics and How it Works

There are many different types of regression analysis procedures. This book focuses on linear regression analysis, specifically ordinary least squares (OLS). Analysts use this type most frequently. Typically, they'll look towards least squares regression first, and then use other types only when there are issues that prevent them from using OLS.

Even when you need to use a different variety of regression, understanding linear regression is crucial. Much of the knowledge about fitting models, interpreting the results, and checking assumptions for linear models that you will learn throughout this book also apply in some fashion to other types of regression analysis. In short, this book provides a broad foundation on the core type of regression, and it's also informative about using more specialized types of regression.

In later chapters, we'll cover possible reasons for using other kinds of regression analysis. I'll ensure that you know when you should consider a specialized type of analysis, and give you pointers about which alternatives to consider for various issues.

We'll start by covering some basic data requirements. Don't confuse these with the analysis assumptions. I discuss those in chapter 9. These data requirements help ensure that you are putting good data into the analysis. You know that old expression, "garbage in, garbage out?" Let's avoid that!

Data Considerations for OLS

To help ensure that your results are valid for OLS linear regression, consider the following principles while collecting data, performing the analysis, and interpreting the results.

The independent variables can be either continuous or categorical.

- Continuous variables can take on almost any numeric value and can be meaningfully divided into smaller increments, including fractional and decimal values. You often measure a continuous variable on a scale. For example, when you measure height, weight, and temperature, you have continuous data.
- Categorical variables have values that you can put into a countable number of distinct groups based on a characteristic. Categorical variables are also called qualitative variables or attribute variables. For example, college major is a categorical variable that can have values such as psychology, political science, engineering, biology, etc.

The dependent variable should be continuous. If it's not continuous, you will most likely need to use a different type of regression analysis (chapter 12) because your model is unlikely to satisfy the OLS assumptions and can produce results that you can't trust.

Use best practices while collecting your data. The following are some points to consider:

- Confirm that the data represent your population of interest.

- Collect a sufficient amount of data that allows you to fit a model which is appropriately complex for the subject area (chapter 8) and provides the necessary precision for the coefficients and predictions (chapters 3 and 10).
- Measure all variables with the highest accuracy and precision possible.
- Record data in the order you collect it. This process helps you assess an assumption about correlations between adjacent residuals (chapter 9).

Now, let's see how OLS regression goes beyond correlation and produces an equation for the line that best fits a dataset.

How OLS Fits the Best Line

Regression explains the variation in the dependent variable using variation in the independent variables. In other words, it predicts the dependent variable for a given set of independent variables.

Let's start with some basic terms that I'll use throughout this book. While I strive to explain regression analysis in an intuitive manner using everyday English, I do use proper statistical terminology. Doing so will help you if you're following along with a college statistics course or need to communicate with professionals about your model.

Observed and Fitted Values

Observed values of the dependent variable are the values of the dependent variable that you record during your study or experiment along with the values of the independent variables. These values are denoted using Y.

Fitted values are the values that the model predicts for the dependent variable using the independent variables. If you input values for the independent variables into the regression equation, you obtain the fitted value. Predicted values and fitted values are synonyms.

An observed value is one that exists in the real world while your model generates the fitted/predicted value for that observation. Standard notation uses $\hat{y}$ to denote fitted values, which you pronounce as Y-hat. In general, hatted values indicate they are a model's estimate for the corresponding non-hatted values.

Residuals: Difference between Observed and Fitted Values

Regression analysis predicts the dependent variable. For every observed value of the dependent variable, the regression model calculates a corresponding fitted value. To understand how well your model fits the data, you need to assess the differences between the observed values and the fitted values. These differences represent the error in the model. No model is perfect. The observed and fitted values will never exactly match. However, models can be good enough to be useful.

This difference is known as a residual, and you'll be learning a lot about them in this book. A residual is the distance between an observed value and the corresponding fitted value. To calculate the difference mathematically, it's simple subtraction:

Residual = Observed value – Fitted value.

Or, written as an equation for the residual, or error, of the ith observation:

$$e_i = y_i - \hat{y}_i$$

Graphically, residuals are the vertical distances between the observed values and the fitted values. On the graph, the line represents the fitted values from the regression model. We call this line . . . the fitted line! The lines that connect the data points to the fitted line represent the residuals.

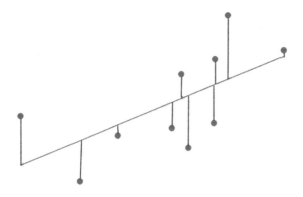

The length of the line is the value of the residual.

It makes sense, right? You want to minimize the distance between the observed values and the fitted values. For a good model, the residuals should be relatively small and unbiased. In statistics, bias indicates that estimates are systematically too high or too low. Unbiased estimates are correct on average.

If the residuals become too large or biased, the model is no longer useful. Consequently, these differences play a vital role during both the model estimation process and later when you assess the quality of the model.

Using the Sum of the Squared Errors (SSE) to Find the Best Line

Let's go back to the height and weight dataset for which we calculated the correlation.

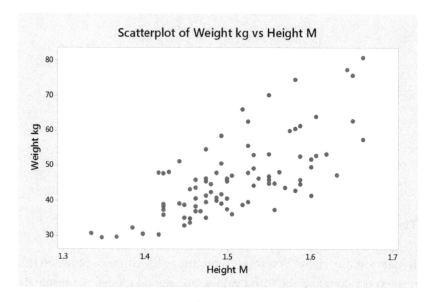

The goal of regression analysis is to draw a line through these data points that minimizes the overall distance of the points from the line. How would you draw the best fitting straight line through this cloud of points?

You could draw many different potential lines. Some observations will fit the model better or worse than other points, and that will vary based on the line that you draw. Which measure would you use to quantify how well the line fits all of the data points? Using what you learned above, you know that you want to minimize the residuals. And, it should be a measure that factors in the difference for all of the points. We need a summary statistic for the entire dataset.

Perhaps the average distance or residual value? If your model has many residuals with values near +10 and -10, that averages to approximately zero distance. However, another model with many residuals near +1 and -1 also averages out to be nearly zero. Obviously, you'd prefer the model with smaller distances. Unfortunately, using the average residual doesn't distinguish between these models.

You can't merely sum the residuals because the positive and negative values will cancel each other out even when they tend to be relatively large. Instead, OLS regression squares those residuals so they're always positive. In this manner, the process can add them up without canceling each other out.

This process produces squared residuals, which statisticians call squared errors. First, we obtain the residuals between the observed and fitted values using simple subtraction, and then we just square them. Simple! A data point with a residual of 3 will have a squared error of 9. A residual of -4 produces a squared error of 16.

Then, the ordinary least squares procedure sums these squared errors, as shown in the equation below:

$$\sum_{i=1}^{n} (y_i - \hat{y}_i)^2$$

Where n equals the number of observations, y_i is the ith observed value, and $\hat{y}_i$ is the corresponding fitted value.

OLS draws the line that minimizes the sum of squared errors (SSE). Hopefully, you're gaining an appreciation for why the procedure is named ordinary *least squares*!

SSE is a measure of variability. As the points spread out further from the fitted line, SSE increases. Because the calculations use squared differences, the variance is in squared units rather the original units of the data. While higher values indicate greater variability, there is no intuitive interpretation of specific values. However, for a given data set, smaller SSE values signal that the observations fall closer to the fitted values. OLS minimizes this value, which means you're getting the best possible line.

In textbooks, you'll find equations for how OLS derives the line that minimizes SSE. Statistical software packages use these equations to solve for the solution directly. However, I'm not going to cover those equations. Instead, it's crucial for you to understand the concepts of residuals and how the procedure minimizes the SSE. If you were to draw any line other than the one that OLS produces, the SSE would increase—which indicates that the distances between the observed and fitted values are growing, and the model is not as good.

Implications of Minimizing SSE

OLS minimizes the SSE. This fact has several important implications.

First, because OLS calculates squared errors using residuals, the model fitting process ultimately ties back to the residuals very strongly. Residuals are the underlying foundation for how least squares regression fits the model. Consequently, understanding the properties of the residuals for your model is vital. They play an enormous role in determining whether your model is good or not. You'll hear so much about them throughout this book. In fact, chapter 9 focuses on them. So, I won't say much more here. For now, just know that you want relatively small and unbiased residuals (positive and negative are equally likely) that don't display patterns when you graph them.

Second, the fact that the OLS procedure squares the residuals has significant ramifications. It makes the model susceptible to outliers and unusual observations. To understand why, consider the following set of residuals: {1 2 3}. Imagine most of your residuals are in this range. These residuals produce the following squared errors: {1 4 9}. Now, imagine that one observation has a residual of 6, which yields a squared error of 36. Compare the magnitude of most squared errors (1 – 9) to that of the unusual observation (36).

To minimize the squared errors, OLS factors in that unusual observation much more heavily than the other data points. The result is that an individual outlier can exert a strong influence over the entire model and, by itself, dramatically change the results. Chapter 9 discusses this problem in greater detail and how to detect and resolve it. For now, be aware that OLS is susceptible to outliers!

Other Types of Sums of Squares

You learned about the error sum of squares, but there are several different types of sums of squares in OLS. We won't focus on the others as much as the SSE, but you should understand what they measure and how they're related:

Sums of Squares	Measures	Calculation
Sum of Squared Errors (SSE)	Overall variability of the distance between the data points and fitted values.	Sum of squared residuals. $$\sum_{i=1}^{n}(y_i - \hat{y}_i)^2$$
Regression Sum of Squares (RSS)	The amount of additional variability your model explains compared to a model that contains no variables and uses only the mean to predict the dependent variable.	Sum of the squared distances between the fitted values and the mean of the dependent variable (y-bar). $$\sum_{i=1}^{n}(\hat{y}_i - \bar{y})^2$$
Total Sum of Squares (TSS)	Overall variability of the dependent variable around its mean.	Sum of the squared distances between the observed values and the mean of the dependent variable. $$\sum_{i=1}^{n}(y_i - \bar{y})^2$$

These three sums of squares have the following mathematical relationship:

RSS + SSE = TSS

Understanding this relationship is fairly straight forward.

- RSS represents the variability that your model explains. Higher is usually good.
- SSE represents the variability that your model does not explain. Smaller is usually good.
- TSS represents the variability inherent in your dependent variable.

Or, Explained Variability + Unexplained Variability = Total Variability

For the same dataset, as you fit better models, RSS increases and SSE decreases by an exactly corresponding amount. RSS cannot be greater than TSS while SSE cannot be less than zero.

Additionally, if you take RSS / TSS, you'll obtain the percentage of the variability of the dependent variable around its mean that your model explains. This statistic is R-squared!

Based on the mathematical relationship shown above, you know that R-squared can range from 0 – 100%. Zero indicates that the model accounts for none of the variability in the dependent variable around its mean. 100% signifies that the model explains all of that variability.

Keep in mind that these sums of squares all measure variability. You might hear about models and variables accounting for variability, and that harkens back to these measures of variability.

We'll talk about R-squared in much greater detail in chapter 6, which helps you determine how well your model fits the data. However, in that chapter, I discuss it more from the conceptual standpoint and what it means for your model. I also focus on various problems with R-squared and alternative measures that address these problems. For now, my goal is for you to understand the mathematical derivation of this useful statistic.

Note: Some texts use RSS to refer to residual sums of squares (which we're calling SSE) rather than regression sums of squares. Be aware of this potentially confusing use of terminology!

Displaying a Regression Model on a Fitted Line Plot

Let's again return to our height and weight data. I'll fit the ordinary least squares model and display it in a fitted line plot. You can use this model to estimate the effect of height on weight. You can also enter height values to predict the corresponding weight. Use the CSV dataset: HeightWeight.

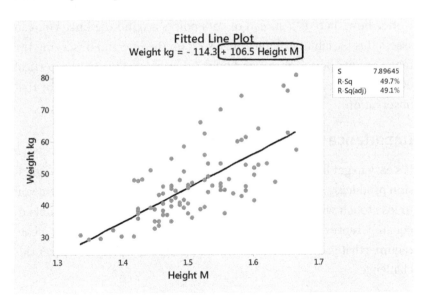

This graph shows all the observations together with a line that represents the fitted relationship. As is traditional, the Y-axis displays the dependent variable, which is weight. The X-axis shows the independent variable, which is height. The line is the fitted line. If you enter the full range of height values that are on the X-axis into the regression equation that the chart displays, you will obtain the line shown on the graph. This line produces a smaller SSE than any other line you can draw through these observations.

Visually, we see that the fitted line has a positive slope that corresponds to the positive correlation we obtained earlier. The line follows the data points, which indicates that the model fits the data. The slope of the line equals the coefficient that I circled. This coefficient indicates how much mean weight tends to increase as we increase height. We can also enter a height value into the equation and obtain a prediction for the mean weight.

Each point on the fitted line represents the mean weight for a given height. However, like any mean, there is variability around the mean. Notice how there is a spread of data points around the line. You can assess this variability by picking a spot on the line and observing the range of data points above and below that point. Finally, the vertical distance between each data point and the line is the residual for that observation.

Importance of Staying Close to Your Data

It's easy to get lost in the large volume of statistical output that regression produces. All of the numerical statistical measures can cause you to lose touch with your data. However, ensuring that your model adequately represents the data, and determining what the results mean, requires that you stay close to the data. Graphs can help you meet this challenge!

I love using fitted line plots to illustrate regression concepts. In my mission to make regression analysis ideas more intuitive, fitted line plots are one of my primary tools. I'll summarize the concepts that fitted line plots illustrate below, but I'll come back to each one later in the book to explore them in more detail.

Fitted line plots are great for showing the following:

- The regression coefficient in the equation corresponds to the slope of the line. What does it mean?
- For different models, the data points vary around the line to a greater or lesser extent, which reflects the precision of the predictions and goodness-of-fit statistics, like R-squared. We'll explore this in more detail because the implications of this precision are often forgotten. How precise are your model's predictions?
- Does the fitted line fit curvature that is present in the data? For now, we're fitting a straight line, but that might not always be the case! Fitted line plots make curvature unmistakable.

As fantastic as fitted line plots are, they can only show simple regression models, which contain only one independent variable. Fitted line plots use two axes—one for the dependent variable and the other for the independent variable. Consequently, fitted line plots are great for displaying simple regression models on a screen or printed on paper. However, each additional independent variable requires another axis or physical dimension. With two independent variables, we can use a 3D representation for it. Although, that's beyond my abilities for this book. With three independent variables, we'd need a four-dimensional plot. That's not going to happen!

If you have a simple regression model, I highly recommend creating a fitted line plot for it and assessing the bullet points above. You'll obtain an excellent overview of how your model fits the data because they're graphed together. However, for multiple regression, we can't use fitted line plots to obtain that overview. For those cases, I'll show you other methods throughout this book for answering those questions. Sometimes these methods will be statistical measures, but whenever possible I'll show you special types of graphs because they bring it to life. These graphical tools include main effects plots, interaction plots, and various residual plots.

Review and Next Steps

In this chapter, I explained how learning about ordinary least squares linear regression provides an excellent foundation for learning about regression analysis. Not only is it the most frequently used type of regression, but your knowledge of OLS will help inform your usage of other types of regression. I showed you some foundational data considerations to keep in mind so you can avoid the problem of "garbage in, garbage out!"

You learned the basics of how OLS minimizes the sums of squared errors (SSE) to produce the best fitting line for your dataset. And, how SSE fits it in with two other sums of squares, regression sums of squares (RSS) and total sums of squares (TSS). In the process, you even got a sneak peek at R-squared (RSS / TSS)!

Then, we explored the height-weight regression model using a fitted line plot.

From here, we'll move on to learning how to interpret the different types of effects for continuous and categorical independent variables, the constant, what statistical significance indicates in this context, and determining significance.

CHAPTER 3

Interpreting Main Effects and Significance

One of the primary goals of a regression model is to describe the relationships in your data. What are the effects your independent variables have on the dependent variable? In this chapter and several more later in the book, you'll learn how to interpret different types of relationships and determine whether they are statistically significant. This process involves assessing the regression coefficients and p-values.

Regression analysis is like other inferential methodologies. Our goal is to draw a random sample from a population and use it to estimate the properties of that population. The coefficients in a regression equation are estimates of the relationships, or effects, that exist in the entire population. In other words, the coefficients are sample estimates of the population parameters. We'll never know the actual population parameters because it's infeasible to measure an entire population. However, inferential procedures estimate these parameters along with a margin of error, which enables the analysis to determine statistical significance.

We want these coefficient estimates to be the best possible estimates of the real population values. What properties do the best estimates have?

Suppose you request an estimate—say for the cost of a service that you are considering. How would you define a reasonable estimate?

The estimates should tend to be right on target. They should not be systematically too high or too low. In other words, they should be unbiased or correct on average.

Recognizing that estimates are almost never exactly correct, you want to minimize the discrepancy between the estimated value and actual value. Large differences are bad!

Small errors that are unbiased are exactly what we need for our coefficient estimates!

When your regression model satisfies the OLS assumptions, which chapter 9 covers, the procedure generates unbiased coefficient estimates that tend to be relatively close to the actual population values (minimum variance). When you violate the assumptions, your results might not be trustworthy.

Regression Notation

Before we move on, let's briefly cover some standard regression notation for ordinary least squares regression. The following notation applies to regression models for entire populations with k independent variables. You can think of these as the ideal models that you'd obtain if you could measure an entire population.

$$y = \beta_0 + \beta_1 X_1 + \cdots + \beta_k X_k + \varepsilon$$

In this notation,

- Y represents the dependent variable.
- The betas (β) represent the true population parameters. β_0 is the constant while the other betas are for the independent variables.
- X's are the independent variables.
- Epsilon (ε) represents the error, which is the left-over random portion of variability that the model can't explain.

However, you'll never work with an entire population. Instead, you'll use samples to estimate the population parameters. The notation for a regression model based on a sample is the following:

$$\hat{y} = \hat{\beta}_0 + \hat{\beta}_1 X_1 + \cdots + \hat{\beta}_k X_k + \hat{\varepsilon}$$

In this notation, the hats represent sample estimates of the population values.

- Y-hat represents the fitted value for the dependent variable. When you enter values for the independent variables into a regression equation, you obtain the fitted value of the dependent variable.
- The beta-hats represent the estimates of population parameters. These estimates are the regression coefficients that appear in your output.
- Epsilon-hat represents the estimate of the error, which we call residuals.

Fitting Models is an Iterative Process

It was difficult determining the order of the chapters that discuss how to interpret the regression results, how to specify the model, and how to check the assumptions. An interactive process interconnects these chapters. You can use the regression output to help you specify the correct model. Assessing the assumptions can also help you specify the right model. Furthermore, if your model doesn't satisfy the assumptions, you can't trust the results. Finally, the various statistics in the output can help you determine how well the model fits the data.

Because these issues are so closely related, it's hard to determine which to discuss first! Ultimately, I'm going with this order:

- Interpreting regression statistics (Chapters 3 – 6).
- Specifying the model (Chapters 7 – 8).
- Checking the assumptions (Chapter 9).

It makes sense to talk about the interpretation of various regression statistics first because they play such an essential role in specifying the model. Otherwise, I'd be talking about these statistics that wouldn't mean anything to you!

However, keep in mind that the entire process is iterative. You'll specify a model, look at your statistical results, check the assumptions, and then change the model accordingly. Importantly, don't trust your statistical results before checking the assumptions. Assumption violations can produce untrustworthy results!

Three Types of Effects in Regression Models

In this chapter, you'll learn about coefficients and p-values for main effects that follow a straight line and for categorical variables. These are the basic relationships in linear regression. In later chapters, we'll cover more complex relationships that you can model.

Throughout this book, I'll cover the following three types of effects that you can model using regression analysis:

- **Main effects**: The relationship between an independent variable and the dependent variable *does not* depend on the value of other variables in the model. (This chapter.)

- **Curvilinear effects**: The relationship between an independent variable and the dependent variable changes based on the value of that independent variable itself. Instead of following a straight line on a graph, these relationships follow curves.
- **Interaction effects**: The relationship between an independent variable and the dependent variable depends on the value of at least one other independent variable in the model.

Additionally, for main effects and interaction effects, the interpretation differs for continuous versus categorical variables. On the other hand, curved relationships can exist only for continuous data.

I'll also cover the constant, which really isn't an effect, but it almost always appears in your statistical output.

Main Effects of Continuous Variables

Main effects for continuous variables that follow a straight line are the bread and butter of regression results. For this type of effect, you simply include the continuous variable in your model. They're the most common type of relationship you'll see in regression models.

What does a straight-line main effect for continuous variables represent?

Suppose you include A and B in your model as independent variables, they're both statistically significant, and the model provides a good fit for your data. In this scenario, you can conclude that the effect of variable A on the dependent variable does not change based on the value of B, and that A's effect is consistent throughout the range of values for A. The same interpretation applies to the effect of variable B—it does not depend on A, and it remains consistent.

Coefficients and p-values in regression analysis work together to tell you which relationships in your model are statistically significant and the nature of those relationships. The coefficients represent a variable's effect and describe the magnitude and direction of the relationship between each independent variable and the dependent variable. Coefficients are the numbers in the regression equation that multiply the values of the variables. The p-values for the coefficients indicate whether these relationships are statistically significant.

The sign of a regression coefficient tells you whether there is a positive or negative correlation between each independent variable and the dependent variable. A positive coefficient indicates that as the value of the independent variable increases, the mean of the dependent variable also tends to increase. A negative coefficient suggests that as the independent variable increases, the dependent variable tends to decrease.

The coefficient value signifies how much the mean of the dependent variable changes given a one-unit shift in the independent variable while holding other variables in the model constant. This property of holding the other variables constant is crucial because it allows you to assess the effect of each variable in isolation from the others.

Graphical Representation of Regression Coefficients

A simple way to grasp regression coefficients and how they relate to the data is to display them on a fitted line plot. Towards this end, we'll revisit the height-weight dataset. The fitted line plot illustrates this by graphing data points along with the relationship between a person's height (IV) and weight (DV). The numeric output and the graph display information from the same model. Again, use the CSV dataset: HeightWeight.

```
Coefficients

Term          Coef    SE Coef          T       P
Constant   -114.326   17.4425   -6.55444   0.000
Height M    106.505   11.5500    9.22117   0.000
```

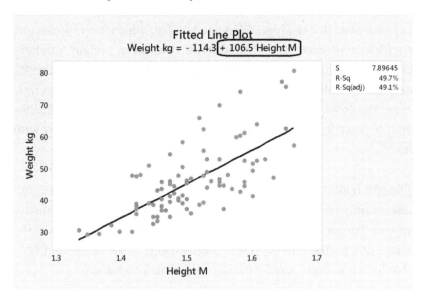

The height coefficient in the regression equation is 106.5. This coefficient represents the mean increase of weight in kilograms for every additional one meter in height. This study sampled preteen girls in the United States. Consequently, if a preteen girl's height increases by 1 meter, the average weight increases by 106.5 kilograms.

The regression line on the graph visually displays the same information. If you move to the right along the x-axis by one meter, the line increases by 106.5 kilograms. Keep in mind that it is only safe to interpret regression results within the observation space of your data. And, we wouldn't want to apply the model outside the target population of preteen girls. We don't know the nature of the relationship between the variables outside the range and population of our dataset. It might change.

In this case, the height and weight data were collected from middle-school girls and range from approximately 1.3 m to 1.7 m. Consequently, we can't shift along the line by a full meter for these data.

Let's suppose that the regression line was flat, which corresponds to a coefficient of zero. For this scenario, the mean weight wouldn't change no matter how far along the line you move. A change in height does not correlate to a change in weight when the coefficient is near zero. That's why a near zero coefficient suggests there is no effect—and, as you'll learn, has a high (insignificant) p-value to go along with it.

The plot really brings this to life. However, two-dimensional plots can display only results from simple regression—one predictor and the response. For multiple linear regression, the interpretation remains the same—the coefficients represent mean change in the dependent variable for a one-unit increase in the independent variable.

Confidence Intervals for Regression Parameters

From basic statistics, you might remember the difference between a point estimate for a population parameter and a confidence interval. If you collect a random sample and calculate the mean, the sample mean is the point estimate for the population mean. You'll never know the exact value of the population parameter because you'll only ever be working with samples. Furthermore, thanks to random sampling error, your sample estimate will not equal the parameter exactly. Unfortunately, the point estimate doesn't indicate how far from the population parameter it is likely to be.

Fortunately, you can calculate confidence intervals for population parameters. A confidence interval is derived from a sample and provides a range of values that likely contains the unknown value of a population parameter. For example, a confidence interval of [9 11] indicates that the population mean is likely to be between 9 and 11. Different random samples drawn from the same population are liable to produce slightly different intervals. If you draw many random samples and calculate a confidence interval for each sample, a specific proportion of the ranges contains the population parameter. That percentage is the confidence level.

For example, a 95% confidence level suggests that if you draw 20 random samples from the same population, you'd expect 19 of the confidence intervals to include the population value, as shown below.

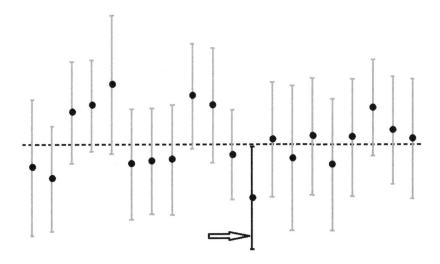

The confidence interval procedure provides meaningful estimates because it produces ranges that usually contain the parameter. You can also see how far your point estimate is likely to be from the parameter value.

In the regression context, remember that we're using our sample to calculate the regression coefficients (β-hats), which are the point estimates of the population parameters (βs). Our sample's estimate of the height coefficient is 106.5. However, if we collect multiple random samples from the same population, each sample will produce its own estimate for the height coefficient. And, we don't know the real value.

How close to the actual population value is our estimate likely to be? To answer this question, have your software calculate the confidence intervals for the regression coefficients. Below is the confidence interval output for the height and weight model.

```
Coefficients

Term        Coef  SE Coef      95% CI     T-Value   P-Value   VIF
Constant  -114.3     17.4  (-149.0, -79.7)   -6.55     0.000
Height M   106.5     11.6  ( 83.5, 129.5)     9.22     0.000  1.00
```

We can be 95% confident that the actual population value for the height coefficient is between 83.5 and 129.5.

When a CI excludes zero, the results are statistically significant. A 95% confidence interval will always agree with a hypothesis test that uses a significance level of 0.05. In the output above, the CI excludes zero, which corresponds to the p-value (0.000) that is less than the significance level (0.05). I'll cover p-values, and the importance of the value zero soon!

The width of a confidence interval reveals the precision of the estimate. Narrower ranges suggest a more precise estimate. In future chapters, when we get into specifying the model and various difficulties, I'll refer to situations, such as overfitting and multicollinearity, that decrease the precision of your model's estimates. You can evaluate this precision by assessing these confidence intervals. For example, if you add more variables to the model and these confidence intervals become wider, you know there is a problem because the additional variables reduce the model's precision.

Example Regression Model with Two Linear Main Effects

Let's interpret the results for the following multiple regression example:

Air Conditioning Costs\$ = 2 * Temperature C − 1.5 * Insulation CM

In this model, we are using the temperature in Celsius and Insulation thickness in centimeters, our two independent variables, to explain air conditioning costs in dollars (dependent variable).

The coefficient sign for Temperature is positive, which indicates a positive relationship between Temperature and Costs. As the temperature increases, so does air condition costs. More specifically, the coefficient value of 2 indicates that for every 1 C increase, the average air conditioning cost increases by two dollars.

On the other hand, the negative coefficient for insulation represents a negative relationship between insulation and air conditioning costs. As insulation thickness increases, air conditioning costs decrease. For every 1 CM increase, the average air conditioning cost drops by $1.50.

Additionally, these are both main effects, which indicates that if you change the value of, say, insulation, the relationship between temperature and air condition costs remains the same. And, these are linear effects. For every 1 C increase in temperature, air condition costs will always increase by $2. It doesn't matter if temperature increases from 20 to 21 C or from 30 to 31 C. That extra degree costs you $2!

However, you can't extend that interpretation outside the range of your data. If you only measured up to 30 C, you can't assume that the same relationship holds true at 35 C.

Interpreting P-Values for Continuous Independent Variables

As I mentioned, regression analysis is a form of inferential statistics where you use a sample to draw conclusions about an entire population. Sample error can produce apparent effects in the sample that don't exist in the population. P-values and significance levels help you determine whether the relationships that you observe in your sample also exist in the larger population.

The p-value for each independent variable tests the null hypothesis that the variable has no relationship with the dependent variable. If there is no relationship, there is no association between the changes in the independent variable and the shifts in the dependent variable. Mathematically, a coefficient of zero represents no effect. Consequently, the hypothesis test assesses whether your sample provides enough evidence to conclude that the population value for the coefficient does not equal zero.

The hypotheses for the independent variables are the following:

- **Null hypothesis**: The coefficient for the independent variable equals zero (no relationship).
- **Alternative hypothesis**: The coefficient for the independent variable does not equal zero.

If the p-value for a variable is less than your significance level, your sample data provide enough evidence to reject the null hypothesis for the entire population. Your data favor the hypothesis that there *is* a non-zero correlation. Changes in the independent variable *are* associated with changes in the response at the population level. This variable is statistically significant and probably a worthwhile addition to your regression model. Significance levels of 0.05 are the most common value.

On the other hand, a p-value that is greater than the significance level indicates that there is insufficient evidence in your sample to conclude that the coefficient doesn't equal zero.

The regression output example below shows that the South and North predictor variables are statistically significant because their p-values equal 0.000. On the other hand, East is not statistically significant because its p-value (0.092) is greater than the usual significance level of 0.05.

```
Coefficients

Term          Coef   SE Coef          T        P
Constant   389.166   66.0937     5.8881    0.000
East         2.125    1.2145     1.7495    0.092
South        5.318    0.9629     5.5232    0.000
North      -24.132    1.8685   -12.9153    0.000
```

Analysts use coefficient p-values as one factor in deciding whether to include variables in the final model. For the results above, we would consider removing East. Keeping variables that are not statistically significant can introduce more error into the model. Statisticians refer to the process of choosing which variables to include in the model as model specification. Chapter 7 discusses model specification in detail.

Regression analysis is all about determining how changes in the independent variables correlate with changes in the dependent variable. Coefficients tell you about these changes and p-values indicate whether these coefficients are significantly different from zero.

Recoding Continuous Independent Variables

The previous examples use the raw values of the independent variables to fit the model. For instance, the height and weight model use the actual height and weight values for each subject. Using the raw values is often appropriate, and it allows for the most natural interpretation of the results. Most of the examples in this book use raw values.

However, analysts sometimes recode their data to obtain valuable benefits. Recoding involves taking the original values and mathematically converting them to other values. While these recoding methods cause you to interpret some of the results differently, the p-values and goodness-of-fit measures remain the same when you fit the same model.

In this section, I discuss standardization and centering, which are two common coding methods.

Standardizing the Continuous Variables

Standardizing your continuous data can be helpful in some circumstances. To standardize a variable, you take each observed value for a variable, subtract the variable's mean, and then divide by the variable's standard deviation. When you standardize a variable, the coded value denotes where the observation falls in the distribution of values by indicating the number of standard deviations above or below the variable's mean. The sign indicates whether the observation is above or below the mean, and the number indicates the number of standard deviations.

Suppose we have a length measurement, and the mean length is 10 and the standard deviation is 3.

Let's standardize the value of three length observations to show how this works: (raw value – variable mean) / variable standard deviation.

- 16: $(16 - 10) / 3 = 2$
- 10: $(10 - 10) / 3 = 0$
- 7: $(7 - 10) / 3 = -1$

The first observation has a raw length value of 16, which is recoded to a standardized value of 2. This value indicates that the observation has a length that is 2 standard deviations above the mean length.

The second observation has an uncoded value of 10 and a standardized value of 0. Standardized values of zero indicate that the original value is precisely equal to the mean. Values relatively close to zero are close to the mean. Higher absolute values indicate that observations are further away.

The third raw value is 7, which is recoded to a standardized value of -1. This observation is one standard deviation below the mean.

Fortunately, with modern statistical software, you don't need to re-code the variables yourself. Usually, you choose an option for standardized coefficients and the software recodes the variables behind the scenes, fits the model using the standardized variables, and displays the standardized coefficients.

Interpreting Standardized Coefficients

When you fit the model using standardized independent variables, the coefficients are now standardized coefficients. Note: For some reason, SPSS refers to standardized coefficients as Beta.

Standardized coefficients signify the mean change of the dependent variable given a one standard deviation increase in an independent variable. Let's go back to this example from before but let's have the software calculate standardized coefficients:

Air Conditioning Costs$ = 3 * Temperature C − 4 * Insulation CM

The standardized coefficient for Temperature (3) indicates that for every one standard deviation increase in the temperature, mean air conditioning costs increase by $3. And, for insulation, every one standard deviation increase in thickness reduces costs by $4.

Why Obtain Standardized Coefficients?

Standardization puts all of the variables on the same scale so you can compare the magnitude of the results. In the example above, temperature and insulation thickness are completely different types of variables. Which one has a larger effect? You cannot use regular coefficients to make this determination because they're using entirely different units (Celsius vs. centimeters). However, standardization puts them all on a consistent scale, which allows you to compare the standardized coefficients.

For the air conditioning example, the absolute values of the standardized coefficients indicate that for an increase of one standard deviation, insulation thickness (-4) affects costs more than temperature (3). I write more about this aspect in chapter 11.

Standardizing the values of your continuous variables can also make them easier to understand in some cases. Temperature in Celsius and thickness in centimeters are both concrete, easy to understand measurements. However, some variables might have meaningless units and can be difficult to understand.

Imagine you're working with a psychological scale for anxiety that extends from 12 to 48. What does a one-unit increase represent? What's considered a substantial change using these meaningless units? You can't answer either of these questions without understanding the full distribution of scores. Using standardized values and standardized coefficients removes the meaningless units and allows you to compare scores to the entire distribution of scores.

Centering Your Continuous Variables

The method of centering variables is related to standardization. This method just subtracts the mean, but it does not divide by the standard deviation. Unlike standardization, centering does not change the interpretation of the coefficients. However, it produces a potentially useful change in interpreting the constant, which I discuss later in the chapter. It also helps reduce a type of multicollinearity, as I show in chapter 9. So, we'll come back to centering later on.

Let's move away from continuous variables and talk about categorical independent variables!

Main Effects of Categorical Variables

Categorical variables, also known as nominal variables, have values that you can put into a countable number of distinct groups based on a characteristic. For categorical variables, you have the variable name and the levels of that variable. The following table shows examples of several categorical variables and their levels.

Variable	College Major	Genre	Gender
Level	Psychology	Science Fiction	Male
Level	Political Science	Drama	Female
Level	Engineering	Comedy	
Level	Statistics		

With continuous variables, you can plot them on a scatterplot and see how one variable changes as you increase the value of the other variable. However, with categorical variables, you're dealing with groups in your data that you cannot incrementally increase. Consequently, you interpret categorical variables differently in regression analysis. The levels of categorical variables represent groups in your data, and you can plot them using a boxplot, as shown below. Regression analysis estimates the mean differences between these groups and determines whether they are statistically significant.

These effects are main effects, which indicates that the effect sizes do not change based on the values of the other variables in the model.

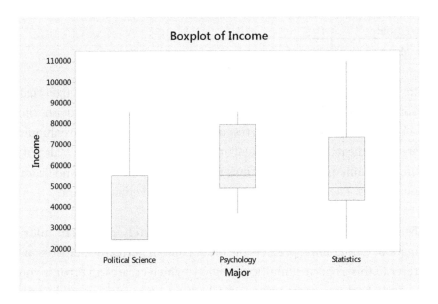

Including categorical variables in a regression model allows you to determine whether the differences in this type of graph are statistically significant while controlling for other variables in the model. Later in this section, we'll analyze the data that this boxplot represents to determine whether the differences between the mean incomes of these groups are statistically significant.

Coding Categorical Variables

Statistical software can't take a categorical variable and directly analyze it. Instead, it converts categorical variables into indicator variables using a (0, 1) coding scheme. Indicator variables, also known as dummy variables, are columns of 1s and 0s that indicate the presence or absence of a characteristic. A 1 indicates the presence of a feature while a 0 represents its absence. The number of indicator variables depends on the number of categorical levels. To show you how this works, I'll start with gender.

Gender	Male	Female
Male	1	0
Female	0	1
Female	0	1
Male	1	0

In the table, the Gender column represents the categorical data that you enter into the worksheet. The value depends on the gender of the subject for which the row corresponds. The Male and Female columns are the indicator variables based on the Gender column. The Male column contains 1s for observations that correspond to males and 0s for non-males. The opposite pattern applies to the Female column.

Notice how these two columns supply completely redundant information? One column predicts the other column perfectly. Statisticians refer to this as perfect multicollinearity, which creates an error if you include both in a regression model. For a categorical variable, you must omit one of the underlying indicator variables from the model, which becomes the reference level.

Let's look at College Major, which has three levels in our example.

College Major	Psychology	Political Science	Statistics
Statistics	0	0	1
Psychology	1	0	0
Statistics	0	0	1
Political Science	0	1	0
Psychology	1	0	0

In this table, College Major is the categorical variable, and the other columns are the indicator variables. Each cell in an indicator variable column contains 1s only when that property is present and a 0 otherwise. For each row, there must be a single value of 1, and all the other values are 0s. In other words, the groups are mutually exclusive. Each subject can belong to one, and only one, of the groups. For example, the first row corresponds to a subject who is majoring in Statistics. Consequently, only the Statistics column contains a 1, and the other columns all contain 0s.

As with Gender, if you include all the indicator variables, you are supplying redundant information, and the software can't perform the analysis. If you look at any two college major columns, you can always figure out the value of the third column. Suppose we exclude the Psychology column. In the first row, we see the 1 under statistics, so we know that Psychology must be zero. In the second row, Political Science and Statistics have 0s. Consequently, Psychology must have a 1. Again, we'll have to remove one indicator variable to perform the analysis. That column becomes the reference level.

For all categorical variables, you must always remove one level from the analysis and use it as the reference level—which we'll discuss in detail later.

As you can see, when you remove one indicator variable from the model, you're altering the data that the software uses during the model fitting process. Consequently, the coefficients and p-values can change. However, using a different reference level does not change the overall story and overall statistical significance.

If your variable has a natural baseline level, or a logical category for comparison, using that level as the reference level will make the interpretation more natural. Statistical software usually chooses a reference level for you. If you want to use a particular reference level, you might need to tell the software which one to use.

With modern software, this coding process occurs behind the scenes, so don't worry about doing this manually. At most, you'll need to specify a reference level. However, I remember the "old days" when I had to create the indicator variables myself! While you won't have to create these variables, it's instructive to know how it works so you understand:

- The requirement for having a reference level.
- How including one categorical variable in your datasheet typically brings multiple indicator variables into the model.

Interpreting the Results for Categorical Variables

Statistical software typically performs several tests on categorical variables. Because one categorical variable often represents multiple indicator variables, the software performs an F-test on that group of indicator variables. Unlike t-tests, F-tests can evaluate multiple model terms simultaneously, which allows them to compare the fits of different linear models. In this situation, an F-test compares the fit of the model with the set of indicator variables that corresponds to a categorical variable to a model without that set of indicator variables. The hypotheses for this F-test are the following:

- **Null**: The model with the categorical variable does not improve the fit of the model compared to the model without the categorical variable.
- **Alternative**: The model with the categorical variable fits the data better than the model without the categorical data.

If your p-value is less than the significance level, you can reject the null hypothesis and conclude that the categorical variable taken as a whole improves the fit of the model.

Next, the analysis compares each factor level to the reference level using t-tests. While the F-test tells you about the categorical variable as a whole, t-tests allow you to explore the differences between the group means and the reference level. The coefficients represent the difference between each level mean and the reference level mean. Use the p-value to determines whether that difference is statistically significant.

The hypotheses for these t-tests are the following:

- **Null**: The difference between the level mean and reference level mean equals zero.
- **Alternative**: The difference between the level mean and reference level mean does not equal zero.

Consequently, if your p-value is less than your significance level, you can reject the null hypothesis and conclude that the level mean is significantly different from the reference level mean. Because these are main effects, the sizes of the effects do not change based on the values of other variables in the model.

Let's take a look at some output and interpret the results!

Example of a Model with a Categorical Variable

Imagine that we want to determine whether college major relates to income. In this example, we'll include College Major as a categorical variable that has three levels: Statistics, Psychology, and Political Science. The previous boxplot displays the data for these groups. The analysis will determine whether the mean differences between groups in that graph are statistically significant. If you want to try this yourself, use the CSV data file: CategoricalExample.

Additionally, we'll include years of experience as a continuous variable. By adding this variable, we can control for differences in the years of experience that might exist between groups. If the subjects in one major have more years of experience by chance, the mean of that group will appear to be higher, but it would be due to more experience rather than the major itself. However, by including experience, the model controls for that possibility. In other words, we'll learn about income differences by major while holding experience constant.

Finally, imagine that we're studying this research question from the perspective of a statistics department. Consequently, we'll use Statistics as the reference level so we can see how the other majors compare to the Statistics major.

The first output for the analysis that we'll look at is the ANOVA table. Here we find the overall significance of the variables.

```
Analysis of Variance

Source        DF       Adj SS        Adj MS  F-Value P-Value
Regression     3   4768836128    1589612043     3.50   0.030
  Experience   1   2252342774    2252342774     4.96   0.035
  Major        2   3762711560    1881355780     4.14   0.027
Error         26  11809775734     454222144
  Lack-of-Fit 13   7078720982     544516999     1.50   0.239
  Pure Error  13   4731054752     363927289
Total         29  16578611861
```

The continuous variable of years of experience variable is statistically significant. However, let's focus on the categorical variable of Major, which I circled. You can see this variable uses 2 degrees of freedom unlike Experience, which uses only 1. Remember, Major has three levels and we excluded Statistics from the model to use it as the reference level. Consequently, the model includes two indicator variables to represent the entire categorical variable of Major, which explains why it uses two degrees of freedom. If your categorical variable has many levels, it will use many degrees of freedom, which can be problematic when your sample size is small. You'll learn more about this problem of overfitting in a later chapter.

Looking at the circled F-test result in the previous output, we see that Major is statistically significant overall. It improves the fit of the model.

Next, let's explore differences in mean income by major by assessing the coefficients.

```
Coefficients

Term                    Coef  SE Coef  T-Value   P-Value   VIF
Constant               49064     7470     6.57     0.000
Experience              5085     2284     2.23     0.035  1.15
Major
   Political Science  -27195     9813    -2.77     0.010  1.34
   Psychology          -5368     9916    -0.54     0.593  1.27
```

I've circled the output that relates to Major. Because Statistics is the reference level that we excluded from the analysis, the table does not display it. The coefficients for Political Science and Psychology indicate how the mean incomes of these majors compare to the mean income of the Statistics major. The negative coefficients indicate that these majors have lower mean incomes than Statistics.

From the coefficients, we learn the following:

- The mean income for Political Science majors is $27,195 LESS than the mean income for Statistics majors.
- The mean income for Psychology majors is $5,368 LESS than the mean income for Statistics majors.

Next, look at the p-values for the t-tests. These p-values determine whether the mean differences are statistically significant. The political science coefficient is statistically significant. Consequently, we can reject the null hypothesis that the mean difference is zero. We're rejecting the notion that the coefficient can plausibly equal zero even while incorporating a margin of error to account for random sample error. We have sufficient evidence to conclude that these two means are different.

On the other hand, the difference between mean incomes for Psychology and Statistics is not statistically significant. We have insufficient evidence to conclude that these means are different. In other words, the observed difference of -$5368 might represent random error. If we were to collect another random sample and perform the analysis again, this difference might vanish.

If we fit the model using a different reference level, the overall significance of Major in the ANOVA table will remain the same as will the goodness-of-fit measures, like R-squared. On the other hand, the comparisons between specific levels will change because we'd be comparing the majors to a different reference level. For example, if Political Science is the reference level, both Psychology and Statistics have mean incomes that are significantly higher than it. However, the overall picture remains the same. Use the reference level that makes the most intuitive sense for your research question.

A quick word about Experience. As you learned in the continuous variable section, here's how to interpret its positive coefficient. For each one-year increase in experience, mean income increases by an average of \$5085 while holding Major constant. Conversely, the estimates for Major holds constant the years of experience. That's extremely helpful for isolating the effect of each variable.

Now, we'll look at a different way of representing the results in the regression equation when you have categorical variables. As you've seen, membership in different majors relates to different average incomes. For example, Political Science majors have a lower average income than Statistics majors. This average difference is an unchanging -\$27,195. Because that amount does not change, we can subtract it from the constant in the regression equation and create an equation for political science specifically.

More generally, indicator variables will shift the regression line up and down the y-axis for specific groups by the value of the coefficient for the corresponding indicator variable. Consequently, you can obtain separate equations for each categorical level with different constants, as shown below.

```
Regression Equation

Major
Political Science   Income = 21869 + 5085 Experience

Psychology          Income = 43696 + 5085 Experience

Statistics          Income = 49064 + 5085 Experience
```

The differences between the constants correspond to the coefficients for Psychology and Political Science.

Controlling for other Variables

At this point, I'm hoping that the importance of a particular aspect of regression analysis is becoming more evident—the ability to hold constant other variables by including them in the model. In the previous example, you saw how including years of experience allows us to isolate the role of college major by accounting for experience.

Now, imagine your goal is to determine whether males and females are paid differently. Suppose you include gender in the income model and it indicates that the average income for men is significantly higher than the average for women. Arguments might be made that males tend to be in higher paying majors more frequently, have more years of experience, are older, and so on. However, if you include these other variables in the model and the male average continues to be significantly higher, you can conclude that women earn lower average incomes than men *while holding constant these other variables.*

That's powerful stuff!

Blurring the Continuous and Categorical Line

You might think that the question of whether a variable is continuous or categorical is like being pregnant. You're either pregnant or you're not. There's no grey area. However, for the question about continuous or categorical, there can be ambiguity. In some cases, you have some discretion about whether to include a variable as one type or the other.

Over the years, I've been asked about this issue many times. It is confusing. This uncertainty tends to occur in two broad types of scenarios.

In the first scenario, at least one of your independent variables is a count variable or an ordinal variable. These types of variables are discrete, but they do contain information about order, scale, or magnitude. These variables share properties of both categorical variables and continuous variables but aren't quite either one.

- Count variables are non-negative integers. Examples include the number of defects, days in the hospital, and number of treatment sessions.
- Ordinal variables have at least three categories, and the categories have a natural order. The categories are ranked, but the differences between ranks may not be equal. For example, first, second, and third in a race are ordinal data. The difference in time between first and second place might not be the same the difference between second and third place.

In the second scenario, you have a continuous variable, but it uses only a limited number of discrete values chosen by the experimenters. For example, researchers bake cakes at temperatures of 325, 375, and 425 degrees for a study. Or, in a longitudinal study, observations occur at specific intervals: 1 month, 2 months, 3 months, etc.

Determining how to include these variables in the model depends on both the nature of your data and the purpose of your study.

The Case for Including It as a Continuous Variable

When the variable in question has many levels, it might be best to include it as a continuous variable. Your software will estimate a line that fits the relationship between the independent and dependent variable. In this case, you can fit it as a linear function or model curvature that is present. At a bare minimum, your variable must have at least three values to fit a straight line. However, it's hard to determine whether there is a linear trend with only three values. And, fitting curved relationships requires more values.

If your study wants to determine how changes in the independent variable relate to changes in the dependent variable, including the variable as a continuous independent variable allows you to estimate that type of relationship.

The Case for Including It as a Categorical Variable

On the other hand, with fewer levels, you might include it as a categorical variable and have the analysis treat each value as a group. In this case, the procedure estimates a fitted mean for each group and does not consider the order of values. As the number of values increases, it becomes increasingly unwieldy comparing all the differences between means. Additionally, recall from the section about coding categorical variables that you'll use many degrees of freedom when a categorical variable has many levels. This issue can be problematic, particularly when you have a small sample size.

If your study wants to assess group means and differences between means, including the variable in question as a categorical variable allows you to answer these questions.

You probably noticed that I haven't discuss the constant in detail. That's next!

Constant (Y Intercept)

The constant term in regression analysis is the value at which the regression line crosses the y-axis. The constant is also known as the y-intercept. That sounds simple enough, right? Mathematically, the regression constant really is that simple. However, the difficulties begin when you try to interpret the *meaning* of the y-intercept in your regression output.

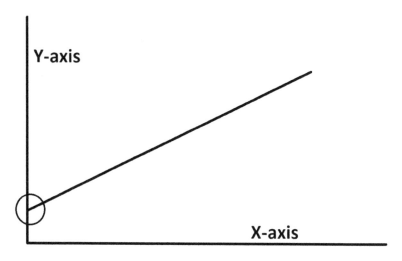

Why is it difficult to interpret the constant term? Because, the y-intercept is almost always meaningless! Surprisingly, while the constant doesn't usually have a meaning, it is almost always vital to include it in your regression models!

The Definition of the Constant is Correct but Misleading

The constant is often defined as the mean of the dependent variable when you set all of the independent variables in your model to zero. In a purely mathematical sense, this definition is correct. Unfortunately, it's frequently impossible to set all variables to zero because this combination can be an impossible or irrational arrangement.

Using the same height-weight dataset as before, the graph below displays the regression model that assesses the relationship between those variables. For this section, I modified the y-axis scale to illustrate the y-intercept, but the overall results haven't changed.

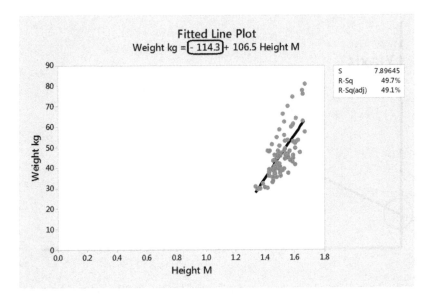

If you extend the regression line downwards until you reach the point where it crosses the y-axis, you'll find that the y-intercept value is negative!

In fact, the regression equation shows us that the negative intercept is -114.3. Using the traditional definition for the regression constant, if height is zero, the expected mean weight is -114.3 kilograms! Huh? Neither a zero height nor a negative weight makes any sense at all!

The negative y-intercept for this regression model has no real meaning, and you should not try attributing one to it.

You think that is a head scratcher? Try imagining a regression analysis with multiple independent variables. The more variables you have, the less likely it is that each and every one of them can equal zero simultaneously.

If the independent variables can't all equal zero, or you get an impossible negative y-intercept, don't interpret the value of the y-intercept!

The Y-Intercept Might Be Outside of the Observed Data

I'll stipulate that, in a few cases, it is possible for all independent variables to equal zero simultaneously. However, to have any chance of interpreting the constant, this all zero data point must be within the observation space of your dataset.

As a general statistical guideline, never make a prediction for a point that is outside the range of observed values that you used to fit the regression model. The relationship between the variables *can* change as you move outside the observed region—but you don't know whether it actually changes because you don't have *that* data!

This guideline comes into play here because the constant predicts the dependent variable for a particular point. If your data don't include the all-zero data point, don't believe the y-intercept.

I'll use the height and weight regression example again to show you how this works. This model estimates its parameters using data from middle school girls whose heights and weights fall within a certain range. We should not trust this estimated relationship for values that fall outside the observed range. Fortunately, for this example, we can deduce that the relationship does change by using common sense.

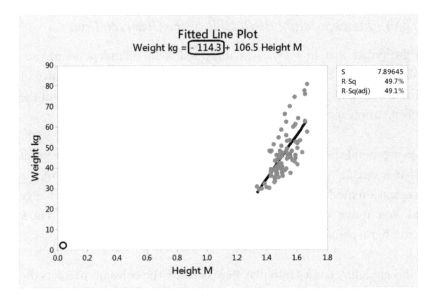

The circle on the bottom left of the graph represents the mean height and weight for a newborn baby. This height isn't exactly zero, but it is as close as possible. By looking at the chart, it is evident that the actual relationship must change over the extended range!

The observed relationship is locally linear, but it must curve as it decreases below the observed values. Don't predict outside the range of your data! This principle is an additional reason why the y-intercept might not be interpretable.

The Constant Absorbs the Bias for the Regression Model

Now, let's assume that all of the independent variables in your model can reasonably equal zero *and* you specifically collect data in that area. You should be good to interpret the constant, right? Unfortunately, the y-intercept might still be garbage!

A portion of the estimation process for the y-intercept is based on the exclusion of relevant variables from the regression model. When you leave relevant variables out, this can produce bias in the model. Bias exists if the residuals have an overall positive or negative mean. In other words, the model tends to make predictions that are systematically too high or too low. The constant term prevents this overall bias by forcing the residual mean to equal zero.

Imagine that you can move the regression line up or down to the point where the residual mean equals zero. For example, if the regression produces residuals with a positive average, just move the line up until the mean equals zero. This process is how the constant ensures that the regression model satisfies the critical assumption that the residual average equals zero. However, this process does not focus on producing a y-intercept that is meaningful for your study area. Instead, it focuses entirely on providing that mean of zero.

The constant ensures the residuals don't have an overall bias, but that might make it meaningless.

Generally, It Is Essential to Include the Constant in a Regression Model

The reason directly above explains why you should almost always have the constant in your regression model—it forces the residuals to have that crucial zero mean.

Furthermore, if you don't include the constant in your regression model, you are actually setting the constant to equal zero. This action forces the regression line to go through the origin. In other words, a model that doesn't include the constant requires all of the independent variables *and* the dependent variable to equal zero simultaneously.

If this isn't correct for your study area, your regression model will exhibit bias without the constant. To illustrate this, I'll use the height and weight example again, but this time I won't include the constant.

```
Regression Equation

Weight kg = 30.8889 Height M

Coefficients

Term            Coef    SE Coef        T         P
Height M    30.8889   0.678630  45.5166   0.000
```

In this output, there is only a height coefficient but no constant.

Now, I'll draw a line based on this equation on the previous graph. This comparison allows us to assess the regression model when we include and exclude the constant.

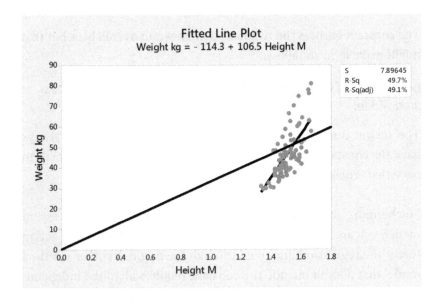

Clearly, the line that goes through the origin does not fit the data at all. Its slope is nowhere close to being correct, and its fitted values are biased.

When it comes to using and interpreting the constant in a regression model, you should almost always include the constant in your regression model even though it is almost never worth interpreting. Statistical software includes the constant in the model by default. Do not change this default unless you have very concrete reasons for doing so.

The key benefit of regression analysis is determining how changes in the independent variables are associated with shifts in the dependent variable. Don't think about the y-intercept too much!

Interpreting the Constant When You Center All the Continuous Independent Variables

Previously, you saw a bunch of reasons for why you usually should not interpret the constant. However, there is one approach that can bypass most, but not all, of the problems I describe.

If you center all of your continuous independent variables, the constant can be meaningful. From earlier in this chapter, recall that centering your variables involves subtracting the mean of each variable from all the values for that variable. Using this approach, zero values for a variable now signify the mean of that variable.

If your model contains only continuous independent variables and you center them, the constant represents the average value of the dependent variable when all the continuous variables are at their means. This information can be useful. Remember that centering the variables does not change the regression coefficients, so you can continue to interpret them in the usual manner.

In the next graph, I refit the height and weight model, but I'll center height on its mean.

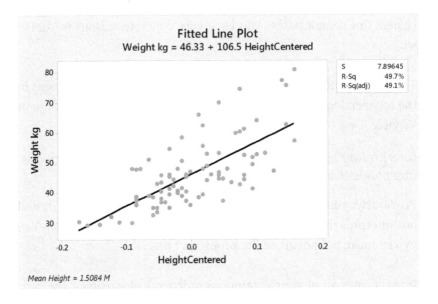

Fitted Line Plot
Weight kg = 46.33 + 106.5 HeightCentered

Mean Height = 1.5084 M

The constant indicates that the mean weight is 46.33 kg at the mean height of 1.5 M. The regression coefficient, its p-value, and the various goodness-of-fit statistics do not change.

This method avoids many of the potential problems with the constant. Zero should be a meaningful value and be within the range of the observations for all independent variables.

However, centering does not eliminate the fact that the constant absorbs the bias of missing independent variables. The estimation process is still going to "float" the regression line up or down so that the mean of the residuals equals zero. Consequently, the value of the constant might not be unbiased. It's hard to know how this factor affects a particular model, but it's something to consider.

If your model contains continuous and categorical independent variables, you'll need to adjust your interpretation of the constant slightly. Recall that OLS includes categorical variables in the model by using a set of indicator variables. When an observation is at the reference level, all of the indicator variables in the model equal zero.

Consequently, when the model includes categorical variables, the constant represents the mean of the dependent variable when:

- All of the continuous variables are at their means, and
- All of the categorical variables are at their reference levels.

Typically, centering refers to the practice of subtracting the mean from each variable. However, you can subtract other values. If another value is more meaningful to your study than the mean, you can subtract that value instead. Just ensure that it is within the range of the data. Suppose a height of 1.25 M is relevant to our study for some reason. If we subtract the value of 1.25 from all heights and fit the model, the constant represents the mean weight for heights of 1.25 meters.

Review and Next Steps

We explored the basics features of linear regression models. You learned how to interpret the coefficients for the main effects of both continuous and categorical variables along with the constant. Together, these parameter estimates form a regression equation. Crucially, you learned how to use p-values to determine whether model terms are statistically significant, and what that means.

In the next two chapters, we'll explore other types of effects that you can model using regression. First, we look at curvature that can be present in the data. So far, we've assessed only data that follow a straight line.

Then, we'll explore interactions where the effect of one variable depends on the value of another variable.

Both curvature and interactions require that you include special terms in your model and change the way you interpret the results.

CHAPTER 4

Fitting Curvature

In regression analysis, curve fitting is the process of specifying the model that provides the best fit to the specific curves in your dataset. Curved relationships between variables are not as straightforward to fit and interpret as linear relationships.

As you saw in the previous chapter, when you increase the independent variable by one-unit for a linear effect, the mean of the dependent variable always changes by a fixed amount that equals the coefficient value. This relationship holds true regardless of where you are in the observation space.

Unfortunately, the real world isn't always nice and neat like that. Sometimes your data have curved relationships between variables. In a curved relationship, the change in the dependent variable associated with a one-unit shift in the independent variable varies based on where you start on the regression line. In other words, the effect of the independent variable is not a constant value.

A quick note about terminology in this chapter. Nonlinear has a very specialized meaning in statistics. Not just any curvature is nonlinear. In fact, linear models can fit curvature. Consequently, I'll use the term curvilinear to described curved relationships in general because non-linear is often incorrect statistically. Don't worry, I'll define linear and nonlinear in the context of regression models in this chapter.

Next up, I'll show you an example of curvature so you can see how it differs from the straight-line relationships you saw earlier. Then, I'll explain a variety of curve fitting methods and show you how to determine whether you're adequately fitting the curvature.

Example Curvature

Linear relationships are relatively straightforward to understand. As you saw in the previous chapter, the mean change in the dependent variable remains constant throughout the regression line. Now, let's move on to interpreting the coefficients for a curvilinear relationship, where the effect depends on your location on the curve. Unfortunately, the interpretation of the coefficients for a curvilinear relationship is less intuitive than linear relationships.

This example uses a quadratic (squared) term to model curvature in the data set. This is one of multiple methods that you'll learn about. You can see that the p-values are statistically significant for both the linear and quadratic terms. But what the heck do the coefficients mean? We cannot interpret them the same way that we do for straight-line relationships.

The regression output below displays the coefficients for a curvilinear relationship.

```
Coefficients

Term                                Coef    SE Coef          T       P
Constant                         7.06962   0.734504    9.62502   0.000
Machine Setting                 -0.69863   0.074321   -9.40015   0.000
MachineSetting*MachineSetting    0.01740   0.001804    9.64557   0.000
```

Graphing the Data for Regression with Polynomial Terms

Graphing the data really helps you visualize the curvature and understand the regression model. You could enter various values for the independent variable into the equation and see how the mean value of the dependent variable changes. Or, just graph it and see it in action!

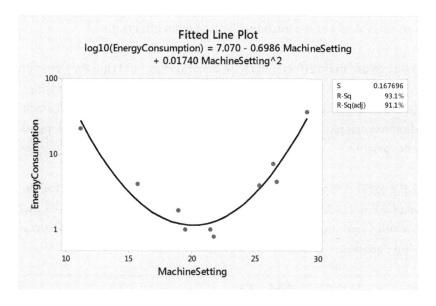

The chart displays the relationship between machine setting and energy consumption. Notice how the effect of machine setting on mean energy usage depends on where you are on the fitted curve. On the x-axis, if you begin with a setting of 12 and increase it by 1, energy consumption decreases. On the other hand, if you start at 25 and increase the setting by 1, energy consumption increases. Near 20 and consumption doesn't change much.

Regression analysis that uses polynomials to model curvature can make interpreting the results trickier. Unlike a linear relationship, the effect of the independent variable changes based on its value. Looking at the coefficients won't make the picture any clearer. Instead, graph the data to truly understand the relationship. Expert knowledge of the study area can also help you make sense of the results.

Graph Curvature with Main Effects Plots

In the previous example, we can graph the curved relationship on a fitted line plot because there is only one independent variable. However, what can you do if your model contains two or more independent variables? Let me introduce you to main effects plots!

You can use main effect plots with linear terms, but I find they're even more valuable when you need to understand curvilinear relationships. Its value lies in the fact that it can graph isolated main effects on a two-dimensional plot even when your model has more than one independent variable.

Let's see this in action. If you want to try this yourself, use the following CSV dataset: Hardness. Suppose we have a regression model that includes two independent variables and obtain the following regression equation:

```
Regression Equation in Uncoded Units

Hardness = -38.8 + 0.759 Temp - 1.60 Pressure + 0.1657 Pressure*Pressure
```

In this model, we're using temperature and pressure in a manufacturing process to predict the hardness of a product. Temperature is a linear term. From the previous chapter, you know that for every one-degree increase in temperature, stiffness increases by 0.759 units of hardness.

Pressure also relates to hardness, but it includes a polynomial term in the portion I circled. How do you interpret this relationship? Because we have two independent variables, we can't graph it using a fitted line plot. The equation has a squared term, like the machine setting example. So, we can guess that density has either a U or inverted U-shaped relationship with temperature. The positive coefficient indicates it is in fact U-shaped.

You could enter different pressure values into the equation over and over to get an idea of how it affects hardness. Or, simply create a main effects plot! To calculate the pressure curve below, the plot's algorithm enters the mean temperature into the equation for the Temp term, and then it cycles through the range of pressure values to calculate the corresponding hardness values. It follows the same process to draw the temperature line.

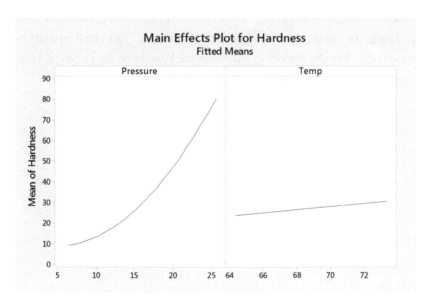

At a glance, you can see the curvilinear nature of the relationship between density and stiffness. Also, notice the linear relationship between temperature and stiffness, which is consistent with its positive, linear coefficient of 0.759.

When there is no relationship between two variables, the plot displays horizontal lines that represents coefficients with values of zero. However, random sampling error can produce apparent relationships in these graphs when two variables are not related. Consequently, while you can use main effects plots to display relationships, use the p-values in the statistical output to verify that they are statistically significant.

When we get to interaction effects in the next chapter, you'll learn about interaction plots, which are similar to these plots.

Why You Need to Fit Curves in a Regression Model

The fitted line plot below illustrates the problem of using a linear relationship to fit a curved relationship. The R-squared is high, but the model is clearly inadequate. The fitted line does not represent the data because the model is systematically incorrect. You must specify a model that fits the curve! We'll come back to these data and try various ways to fit the curve.

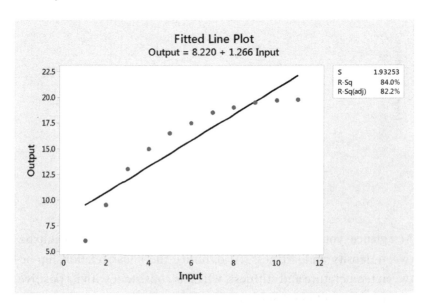

When you have one independent variable, using a fitted line plot both to see curvature in the data and determining whether your model fits the curvature is easy. With multiple regression, main effects plots display how your model fits the curvature. However, these plots don't indicate how *well* your model fits the curvature. For multiple regression, residual plots are a crucial indicator of whether your model adequately fits curved relationships.

If you see a pattern in the residual plots, your model doesn't provide an adequate fit for the data. A common reason is that your model incorrectly models the curvature. Plotting the residuals by each of your independent variables can help you identify curved relationships that you need to model. We'll come back to this method in chapter 9.

In others cases, you might need to depend on subject-area knowledge to fit the curve. Previous experience or research can tell you that the effect of one variable on another varies based on the value of the independent variable. Perhaps there's a limit, threshold, or point of diminishing returns where the relationship changes?

TIP: When you start working with your dataset, the best way to determine whether the relationships between variables are curved is to graph them in a scatterplot. Additionally, the curve that the plot displays often helps you determine how to model it.

The majority of this book focuses on ordinary least squares regression, which is a type of linear model. However, linear models can fit curves. I know, statistics isn't known for terminology that makes sense!

Nonlinear regression is a type of analysis that can fit more types of curves. Consequently, I will show you methods for fitting curves using both linear and nonlinear regression. Nonlinear regression functions very differently than linear regression. For this book, I'm just showing you enough about nonlinear regression so you know when to use it. You're just dipping your toe in it.

Despite the limitations on the types of curves that linear models can fit, I'm always surprised at how often they adequately fit the curvature!

Difference between Linear and Nonlinear Models

The difference between linear and nonlinear regression models isn't as straightforward as it sounds. Over the years, I've seen a lot of confusion over this issue. You'd think that linear equations produce straight lines and nonlinear equations model curvature. Unfortunately, that's *not* correct. Just because you're fitting a curve, it doesn't necessarily mean you're using nonlinear regression. Both types of models can fit curves to your data—so that's not the defining characteristic. In this section, I'll teach you how to identify linear and nonlinear regression models.

The difference between nonlinear and linear is the "non." OK, that sounds like a joke, but, honestly, that's the easiest way to understand the difference. First, I'll define what linear regression is, and then everything else must be nonlinear regression. I'll include examples of both linear and nonlinear regression models.

Linear Regression Equations

A linear regression model follows a very particular form. In statistics, a regression model is linear when all terms in the model are one of the following:

- The constant
- A parameter multiplied by an independent variable (IV)

Then, you build the equation by only adding the terms together. These rules limit the form to just one type:

Dependent variable = constant + parameter * IV + ... + parameter * IV

Or:

$$y = \beta_0 + \beta_1 X_1 + \cdots + \beta_k X_k$$

Statisticians say that this type of regression equation is linear in the parameters. However, it is possible to model curvature with this type of model. While the function must be linear in the parameters, you can raise an independent variable by an exponent to fit a curve. For example, if you square an independent variable, the model can follow a U-shaped curve, as you saw in the preceding section.

$$y = \beta_0 + \beta_1 X_1 + \beta_2 X_1^2$$

While the independent variable is squared, the model is still linear in the parameters. Linear models can also contain log terms and inverse terms to follow different kinds of curves and yet continue to be linear in the parameters.

The following regression example models the relationship between body mass index (BMI) and body fat percent. Later in this book, I use this model to show how to make predictions with regression analysis. It is a linear model that uses a quadratic (squared) term to model the curved relationship.

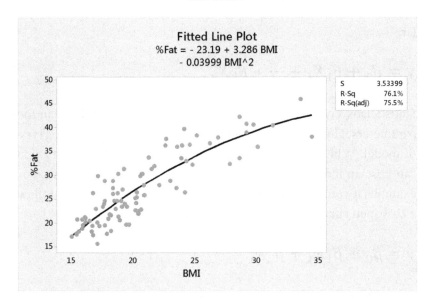

Fitted Line Plot
%Fat = - 23.19 + 3.286 BMI
- 0.03999 BMI^2

S	3.53399
R-Sq	76.1%
R-Sq(adj)	75.5%

Nonlinear Regression Equations

I showed how linear regression models have one basic configuration. Now, we'll focus on the "non" in nonlinear! If a regression equation doesn't follow the rules for a linear model, then it must be a nonlinear model. It's that simple! A nonlinear model is literally not linear.

The added flexibility opens the door to a huge number of possible forms. Consequently, nonlinear regression can fit an enormous variety of curves. However, because there are so many candidates, you may need to conduct some research to determine which functional form provides the best fit for your data.

On the next page, I present a handful of examples that illustrate the diversity of nonlinear regression models. Keep in mind that each function can fit a variety of shapes, and there are many nonlinear functions. Also, notice how nonlinear regression equations are not comprised of only addition and multiplication! Thetas (θ) are the parameters, and Xs are the independent variables.

Example Nonlinear equations

Power

$$\theta_1 * X^\theta 2$$

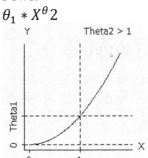

Weibull growth

$$\theta + (\theta_2 - \theta_1) * exp(-\theta_3 * X^\theta 4)$$

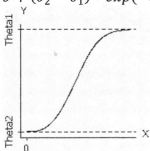

Fourier

$$\theta_1 * cos(X + \theta_4) + \theta_2 * cos(2 * X + \theta_4) + \theta_3$$

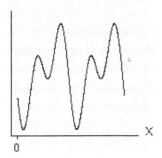

The defining characteristic for both types of models is the functional form. If you can focus on the form that represents a linear model, it's easy enough to remember that anything else must be a nonlinear.

Finding the Best Way to Model Curvature

Let's go back to the example data I showed you at the beginning of this chapter. We'll go over various linear models and a nonlinear model to highlight the different options. I'll also show you how to determine which model provides the best fit.

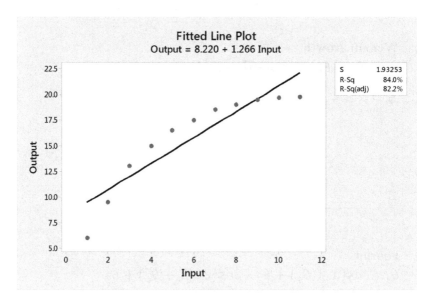

To compare curve fitting methods, I'll fit models to the curve in the fitted line plot above because it is not an easy fit. Let's assume that these data are from a physical process with very precise measurements. We need to produce accurate predictions of the output for any specified input. Use the following CSV dataset for these examples: CurveFittingExample.

To determine which method fits this curve the best, we'll use a combination of graphs and goodness-of-fit statistics. The two statistics we'll use are R-squared and the standard error of the regression (S). I covered the basics of R-squared in chapter 2. We'll go over both statistics, and more, in chapter 6, which is all about goodness-of-fit. For now, keep in mind that higher R-squared values and lower S values are often better.

Curve Fitting using Polynomial Terms in Linear Regression

The most common method to fit a curvilinear relationship is to include polynomial terms in a linear model. If you're unsure where to start for your dataset, polynomials are a great place! Polynomial terms are independent variables that you raise to a power, such as squared or cubed terms. You saw two models with polynomial terms at the beginning of this chapter.

To determine the correct polynomial term to include, simply count the number of bends in the line. Take the number of bends in your curve and add one for the model order that you need. For example, quadratic terms model one bend while cubic terms model two. In practice, cubic terms are very rare, and I've never seen quartic terms or higher.

Tip: If you include a polynomial term in your model, you should center your continuous independent variables to reduce the multicollinearity that it produces. Chapter 9 illustrates this problem and solution.

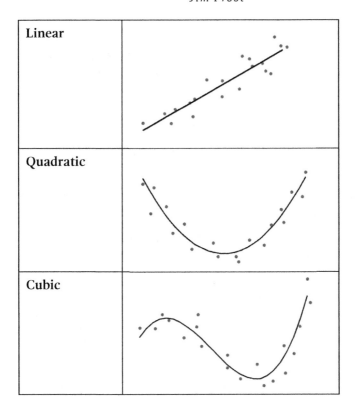

Our data has one bend. Let's fit a linear model with a quadratic term.

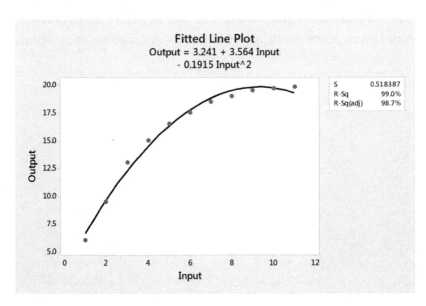

The R-squared has notably increased from 84% to 99%, but the regression line doesn't quite fit correctly. The fitted line systematically over- and under-predicts the data at different points along the curve. The high R-squared reinforces a point I make in chapter 6 about interpreting R-squared. High R-squared values don't always represent good models and that you need to check the residual plots!

While a polynomial didn't work for this model, it's the most common method and works for a surprising number of datasets. Polynomials are usually the place to start. Then consider other methods only when polynomials don't fit the data.

Let's try other models.

Curve Fitting using Reciprocal Terms in Linear Regression

When your dependent variable descends to a floor or ascends to a ceiling (i.e., approaches an asymptote), you can try using a reciprocal of an independent variable (1/X). Use a reciprocal term when the effect of an independent variable decreases as its value increases. To use this method, you need to create a new column in your dataset and use it in the analysis.

$$\frac{\beta * 1}{X}$$

The value of this term decreases as the independent variable (X) increases because it is in the denominator. In other words, as X increases, the effect of this term decreases and the slope flattens. X cannot equal zero for this type of model because you can't divide by zero.

For our data, the increases in Output flatten out as the Input increases. There appears to be an asymptote near 20. Let's try fitting the curve using a reciprocal term. In the data set, I created a column for 1/Input

(InvInput). I fit a model with a linear reciprocal term (top) and another with a quadratic reciprocal term (bottom).

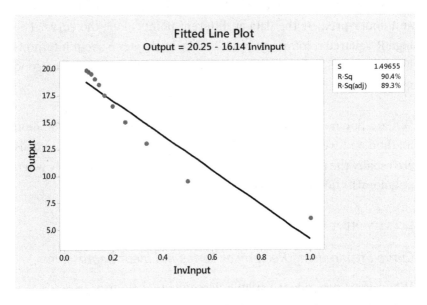

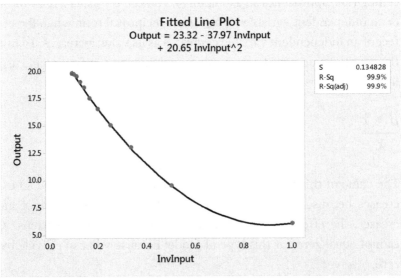

For our example dataset, the quadratic reciprocal model provides a much better fit to the curvature. The plots change the x-axis scale to 1/Input, which makes it difficult to see the natural curve in the data.

To show the natural scale of the data, I created a scatterplot using the regression equations. Clearly, the triangle data points are closer to the inverse quadratic line.

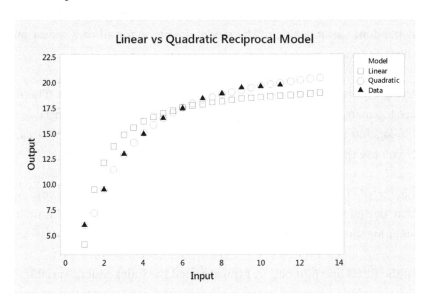

On the fitted line plots, the quadratic reciprocal model has a higher R-squared value (good) and a lower S-value (good) than the quadratic model. It also doesn't display biased fitted values. This model provides the best fit to the data so far!

Curve Fitting with Log Functions in Linear Regression

A log transformation allows linear models to fit curves that are otherwise possible only with nonlinear regression.

For instance, you can express the nonlinear function:

$$Y = e^{B0} X_1^{B1} X_2^{B2}$$

In the linear form:

$$\text{Ln } Y = B_0 + B_1 \ln X_1 + B_2 \ln X_2$$

Your model can take logs on both sides of the equation, which is the double-log form shown above. Or, you can use a semi-log form, which is where you take the log of only one side. If you take logs on the independent variable side of the model, it can be for all or a subset of the variables.

Using log transformations is a powerful method to fit curves. There are too many possibilities to cover them all. Choosing between a double-log and a semi-log model depends on your data and subject area. If you use this approach, you'll need to do some investigation.

Let's apply this to our example curve. A semi-log model can fit curves that flatten as the independent variable increases. Let's see how a semi-log model fits our data!

In the fitted line plot below, I transformed the independent variable.

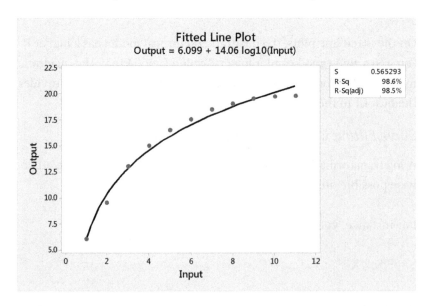

Like the first quadratic model we fit, the semi-log model provides a biased fit to the data points. Additionally, the S and R-squared values are very similar to that model. The model with the quadratic recipro-cal term continues to provide the best fit.

So far, we've performed curve fitting using only linear models. Let's switch gears and try a nonlinear regression model.

Curve Fitting with Nonlinear Regression

Now, we'll take a brief foray into nonlinear regression. If you need to perform nonlinear regression to fit your data, you'll probably need to do some more research. This section shows you its potential.

As you fit regression models, you might need to make a choice be-tween linear and nonlinear regression models. While both types of models can fit curvature, nonlinear regression is much more flexible in the shapes of the curves that it can fit. After all, the sky is the limit when it comes to the possible forms of nonlinear models.

The general guideline is to use linear regression first to determine whether it can fit the particular type of curve in your data. If you can't obtain an adequate fit using one of the methods in linear regression, that's when you might need to choose nonlinear regression.

Linear regression is easier to use, simpler to interpret, and you obtain more statistics that help you assess the model. While linear regression can model curves, it is relatively restricted in the shapes of the curves that it can fit. Sometimes it can't fit the specific curve in your data.

Nonlinear regression can fit many more types of curves, but it can re-quire more effort both to find the best fit and to interpret the role of the independent variables. Additionally, R-squared is not valid for nonlinear regression, and it is impossible to calculate p-values for the parameter estimates.

Nonlinear regression is a very powerful alternative to linear regres-sion. It provides more flexibility in fitting curves because you can choose from a broad range of nonlinear functions. In fact, there are so many possible functions that the trick becomes finding the function that best fits the particular curve in your data.

Most statistical software packages that perform nonlinear regression have a catalog of nonlinear functions. You can use that to help pick the function. Further, because nonlinear regression uses an iterative algorithm to find the best solution, you might need to provide the starting values for all of the parameters in the function.

Our data approach an asymptote, which helps us choose a nonlinear function from the catalog below.

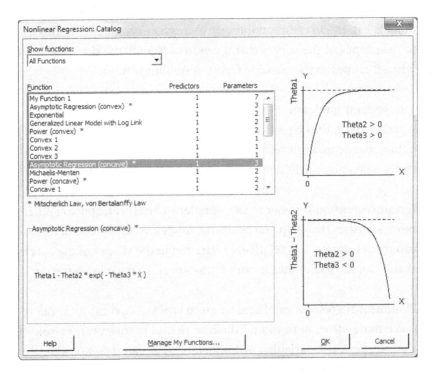

The diagram in the catalog helps us determine the starting values. Theta1 is the asymptote. For our data, that's near 20. Based on the shape of our curve, Theta2 and Theta3 must be both greater than 0.

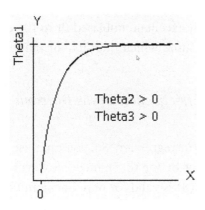

Consequently, I'll use the following starting values for the parameters:

- Theta1: 20
- Theta2: 1
- Theta3: 1

The fitted line plot below displays the nonlinear regression model.

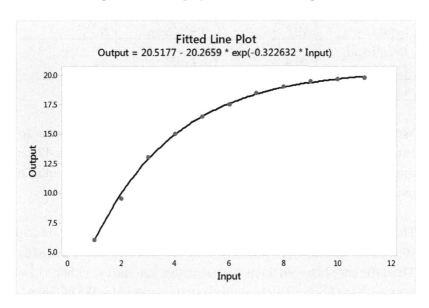

The nonlinear model provides an excellent, unbiased fit to the data. Let's compare models and determine which one fits our curve the best.

Comparing the Curve-Fitting Effectiveness of the Different Models

R-squared is not valid for nonlinear regression. So, you can't use that statistic to assess the goodness-of-fit for this model. However, the standard error of the regression (S) is valid for both linear and non-linear models and serves as great way to compare fits between these types of models. A small standard error of the regression indicates that the data points are closer to the fitted values.

Model	R-squared	S	Unbiased
Reciprocal Quadratic	99.9	0.134828	Yes
Nonlinear	N/A	0.179746	Yes
Quadratic	99.0	0.518387	No
Semi-Log	98.6	0.565293	No
Reciprocal Linear	90.4	1.49655	No
Linear	84.0	1.93253	No

We have two models at the top that are equally good at producing accurate and unbiased predictions. These two models are the linear model that uses the quadratic reciprocal term and the nonlinear model.

The standard error of the regression for the nonlinear model (0.179746) is almost as low the S for the reciprocal model (0.134828). The difference between them is so small that you can use either. However, with the linear model, you also obtain p-values for the independent variables (not shown) and R-squared.

For reporting purposes, these extra statistics can be handy. However, if the nonlinear model had provided a much better fit, we'd choose it even without those statistics.

Closing Thoughts

You can use various methods that collectively provide great flexibility to fit most any type of curve. Further, identifying the best model involves assessing only a few statistics and the residual plots.

Setting up your study and collecting the data is a time intensive process. It's definitely worth the effort to find the model that provides the best fit.

Any time you are specifying a model, you need to let subject-area knowledge and theory guide you. Additionally, some study areas might have standard practices and functions for modeling the data.

Here's one final caution. You'd like a great fit, but you don't want to overfit your regression model. An overfit model is too complex, it begins to model the random error, and it falsely inflates the R-squared. In chapter 6, I'll show you some tools that can help you detect and avoid this problem.

Another Curve Fitting Example

Let's go through one more example using both linear and nonlinear regression. As usual, our goal is to develop an unbiased model. These data are freely available from the NIST and pertain to the relationship between density and electron mobility. Use the CSV data file to try it yourself: ElectronMobility.

Linear model

First, I'll attempt to fit the curve using a linear model. Because there is only one independent variable, I can use a fitted line plot. In this model, I use a cubed term to fit the curvature because there are two bends.

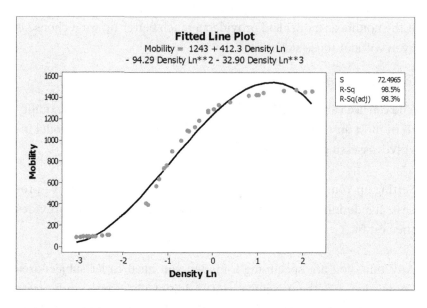

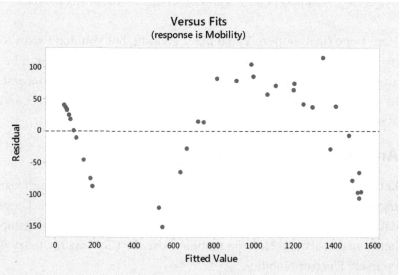

The fitted relationship in the graph follows the data fairly close and produces a high R-squared of 98.5%. Those sound great, but look more closely and you'll notice that various places along the regression line consistently under and over-predict the observed values. This model is biased, and it again illustrates a point that I make in the chapter about goodness-of-fit. By themselves, high R-squared values don't necessarily indicate that you have a good model.

Because we have only one independent variable, we can plot the relationship on the fitted line plot. However, when you have more than one independent variable, you can't use a fitted line plot and you'll need to rely on residual plots to check the regression assumptions. For our data, the residual plots display the nonrandom patterns very clearly. You want to see random residuals.

Our linear regression model can't adequately fit the curve in the data. There's nothing more we can do with linear regression. Consequently, it's time to try nonlinear regression.

Example of a nonlinear regression model

Now, let's fit the same data but using nonlinear regression. As I mentioned earlier, nonlinear regression can be harder to perform. The fact that you can fit nonlinear models with virtually an infinite number of functional forms is both its strength and downside.

The main positive is that nonlinear regression provides the most flexible curve-fitting functionality. The downside is that it can take considerable effort to choose the nonlinear function that creates the best fit for the particular shape of the curve. Unlike linear regression, you also need to supply starting values for the nonlinear algorithm. Some datasets can require substantial effort to find acceptable starting values. For instance, some starting values can cause the algorithm to fail to converge on a solution or to converge on an incorrect solution. It's for these reasons that I always recommend fitting linear models first.

Our example dataset is one that the NIST uses to illustrate a hard-to-fit nonlinear relationship. So, it's no surprise that the linear model was insufficient. Because this section focuses on the basics of choosing between linear and nonlinear models, I'm not going to cover how the researchers chose the optimal functional form of the nonlinear model.

Instead, I'll jump to the solution and not show all the work to get there, much like a cooking show! I want you to see how the following non-linear model compares to the linear model based on the best solution.

For our data, a rational function provides the best nonlinear fit. A rational function is the ratio of two polynomial functions. For electron mobility, the model is:

$$Y = (B1 + B2*x + B3*x^2 + B4*x^3) / (1 + B5*x + B6*x^2 + B7*x^3)$$

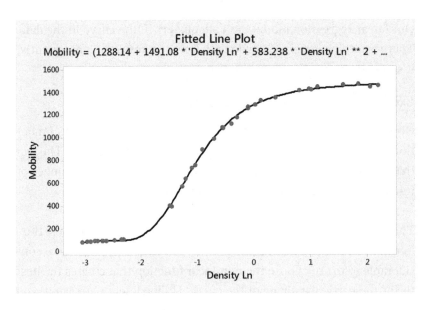

Fitted Line Plot
Mobility = (1288.14 + 1491.08 * 'Density Ln' + 583.238 * 'Density Ln' ** 2 + ...

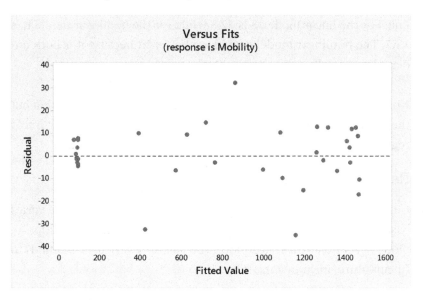

Summary	
Iterations	21
Final SSE	5642.71
DFE	30
MSE	188.090
S	13.7146

The equation for the nonlinear regression analysis is too long for the fitted line plot:

Electron Mobility = (1288.14 + 1491.08 * Density Ln + 583.238 * Density Ln^2 + 75.4167 * Density Ln^3) / (1 + 0.966295 * Density Ln + 0.397973 * Density Ln^2 + 0.0497273 * Density Ln^3)

Comparing the Regression Models and Making a Choice

In the fitted line plot, the nonlinear relationship follows the data almost exactly. The residual plot displays the randomness that we want to see for an unbiased model. R-squared does not appear because it is invalid for nonlinear regression. However, we can compare the standard error of the regression (S) for the two models. You want S to be smaller because it indicates that the data points are closer to the fitted line. For the linear model, S is 72.5 while for the nonlinear model it is 13.7. The nonlinear model provides a better fit because it is both un-biased and produces smaller residuals.

Nonlinear regression is a powerful alternative to linear regression but there are a few drawbacks. Fortunately, it's not difficult to try linear regression first.

Review and Next Steps

Curvature happens when the effect of an independent variable varies based on its own value. It's easiest to detect curved relationships by plotting your data on scatterplots. You can try a variety of methods to fit curvature, including the following:

- Polynomials in linear regression.
- Inverses in linear regression.
- Logs in linear regression.
- Nonlinear regression.

Use main effects plots to see *how* your model fits the curvature. Use fitted line plots, residual plots, and goodness-of-fit statistics, such as R-squared and S, to determine *how well* it fits the data. Collectively, these tools help you decide which approach is best for your data.

Don't rely solely on the goodness-of-fit statistics because even an ex-cellent value doesn't necessarily mean that you fit the curvature ade-quately. Use statistical measures in conjunction with graphs!

Next, I'll cover interaction effects, which occur when the effect of one independent variable depends on the value of a different independent variable.

CHAPTER 5

Interaction Effects

Interaction effects occur when the effect of one variable depends on the value of another variable. In this chapter, I explain interaction effects, how to interpret them in statistical designs, and the problems you will face if you don't include them in your model.

In any study, whether it's a taste test or a manufacturing process, many variables can affect the outcome. Changing these variables can affect the outcome directly. For instance, changing the food condiment in a taste test can affect the overall enjoyment. In this manner, analysts use models to assess the relationship between each independent variable and the dependent variable. This kind of an effect is called a main effect. Main effects do not depend on the value of other variables in the model. Throughout chapters 3 and 4, we assessed main effect, both linear and curvilinear. However, it can be a mistake to assess only main effects.

In more complex study areas, the independent variables might interact with each other. Interaction effects indicate that a third variable influences the relationship between an independent and dependent variable. This type of effect makes the model more complex, but if the real world behaves this way, it is critical to incorporate it in your model. For example, the relationship between condiments and enjoyment probably depends on the type of food—as we'll see!

Example with Categorical Independent Variables

I think of interaction effects as an "it depends" effect. You'll see why! Let's start with an intuitive example to help you understand these effects conceptually.

Imagine that we are conducting a taste test to determine which food condiment produces the highest enjoyment. We'll perform a regression analysis where our dependent variable is Enjoyment. Our two independent variables are both categorical variables: Food and Condiment.

Our model with the interaction term is:

Satisfaction = Food + Condiment + Food*Condiment

The Food*Condiment is the interaction term in the model. Behind the scenes, your statistical software multiplies the two variables to calculate the value for the interaction term.

To keep things simple, we'll include only two foods (ice cream and hot dogs) and two condiments (chocolate sauce and mustard) in our analysis.

Given the specifics of the example, an interaction effect would not be surprising. If someone asks you, "Do you prefer ketchup or chocolate sauce on your food?" Undoubtedly, you will respond, "It depends on the type of food!" That's the "it depends" nature of an interaction effect. You cannot answer the question without knowing more information about the other variable in the interaction term—which is the type of food in our example!

That's the concept. Now, I'll show you how to include an interaction term in your model and how to interpret the results.

How to Interpret Interaction Effects

Let's perform our analysis. Use the CSV data file to try it yourself: Interactions_Categorical.

Enjoyment is the dependent variable while Food and Condiment are the independent variables. The p-values in the output tell us that the interaction effect (Food*Condiment) is statistically significant. Consequently, we know that the satisfaction you derive from the condiment *depends* on the type of food. In other words, the relationship between Condiment and Enjoyment changes based on the value of Food.

```
Factor Information

Factor      Type    Levels  Values
Food        Fixed      2    Hot Dog, Ice Cream
Condiment   Fixed      2    Chocolate Sauce, Mustard

Analysis of Variance

Source            DF     Adj SS   Adj MS  F-Value  P-Value
  Food             1        1.6      1.6     0.06    0.801
  Condiment        1      277.5    277.5    11.07    0.001
  Food*Condiment   1    15695.8  15695.8   626.15    0.000
Error             76     1905.1     25.1
Total             79    17880.0


Coefficients

Term                        Coef  SE Coef  T-Value  P-Value
Constant                  77.320    0.560   138.13    0.000
Food
  Hot Dog                  0.141    0.560     0.25    0.801
Condiment
  Chocolate Sauce          1.863    0.560     3.33    0.001
Food*Condiment
  Hot Dog Chocolate Sauce -14.007    0.560   -25.02    0.000
```

Statistically, it's just as valid to state that the relationship between Food and Enjoyment changes based on the value of Condiment. While both ways of describing the two-way interaction between Food and Condiment are correct, sometimes one is more appropriate given the subject area. For our study, it's more natural to start with the food and then determine which condiment maximizes enjoyment. We don't usually start with a condiment in mind and then pick the food!

But, how do we interpret the interaction effect and truly understand what the data are saying? The best way to understand these effects is with a special type of graph—an interaction plot. This type of plot displays the fitted values of the dependent variable on the y-axis while the x-axis shows the values of the first independent variable. Meanwhile, the various lines represent values of the second independent variable.

On an interaction plot, parallel lines indicate that there is no interaction effect while different slopes suggest that one might be present. Below is the plot for Food*Condiment.

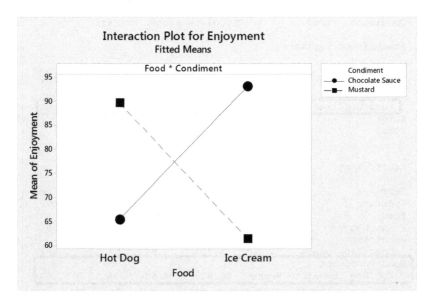

The crossed lines on the graph suggest that there is an interaction effect, which the significant p-value for the Food*Condiment term confirms. The graph shows that enjoyment levels are higher for chocolate sauce when the food is ice cream. Conversely, satisfaction levels are higher for mustard when the food is a hot dog. If you put mustard on ice cream or chocolate sauce on hot dogs, you won't be happy!

Which condiment is best? It depends on the type of food, and we've used statistics to demonstrate this effect.

Overlooking Interaction Effects is Dangerous!

When you have statistically significant interaction effects, you can't interpret the main effects without considering the interactions. In the previous example, you can't answer the question about which condiment is better without knowing the type of food. Again, "it depends."

Suppose we want to maximize satisfaction by choosing the best food and the best condiment. However, imagine that we forgot to include the interaction effect and assessed only the main effects. We'll make our decision based on the main effects plot below.

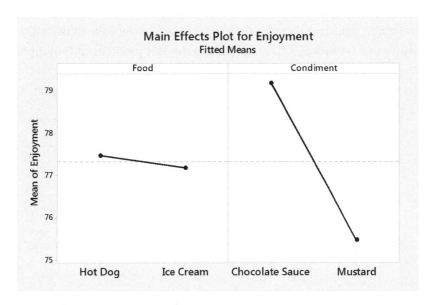

Based on these plots, we'd choose hot dogs with chocolate sauce because they each produce higher enjoyment. That's not a good choice despite what the main effects show! When you have statistically significant interactions, you cannot interpret the main effect without considering the interaction effects.

Given the intentionally intuitive nature of our silly example, the consequence of disregarding the interaction effect is evident at a passing glance. However, that is not always the case, as you'll see in the next example.

Example with Continuous Independent Variables

For our next example, we'll assess continuous independent variables in a regression model for a manufacturing process. The independent variables (processing time, temperature, and pressure) affect the dependent variable (product strength). To follow along, use the CSV data file: Interactions_Continuous.

Tip: If you include an interaction term in your model for continuous variables, you should center these variables to reduce the multicollinearity that it produces. Chapter 9 illustrates this problem and solution.

In the regression model, I'll include temperature*pressure as an interaction effect.

```
Analysis of Variance

Source                DF    Adj SS   Adj MS   F-Value  P-Value
Regression             4   1822.56   455.64    57.13    0.000
  Temperature          1     58.33    58.33     7.31    0.012
  Pressure             1     52.62    52.62     6.60    0.017
  Time                 1   1712.89  1712.89   214.76    0.000
  Temperature*Pressure 1     62.08    62.08     7.78    0.000
Error                 24    191.42     7.98
Total                 28   2013.98


Model Summary

      S   R-sq  R-sq(adj)  R-sq(pred)
2.82417  90.50%    88.91%      81.02%

Regression Equation

Strength = 1064 - 8.54 Temperature - 11.52 Pressure - 4.774 Time
           + 0.1210 Temperature*Pressure
```

The output indicates that the interaction term is statistically significant. But, how do you interpret the interaction coefficient in the regression equation? You could try entering values into the regression equation and piece things together. However, it is much easier to use interaction plots!

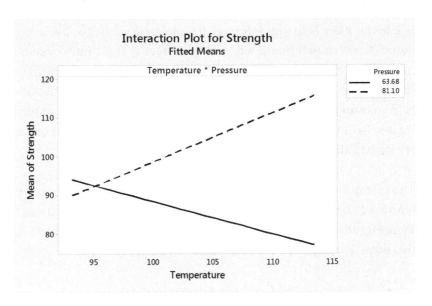

In the interaction plot, the variables are continuous rather than categorical. To produce the plot, the statistical software chooses a high value and a low value for pressure, which are displayed in the legend, and enters them into the regression equation along with the range of values for temperature.

As you can see, the relationship between temperature and strength changes direction based on the pressure. For high pressures, there is a positive relationship between temperature and strength while for low pressures it is a negative relationship. By including the interaction term in the model, you can capture relationships that change based on the value of another variable.

If you want to maximize product strength and someone asks you if the process should use a high or low temperature, you'd have to respond, "It depends." In this case, it depends on the pressure. You cannot answer the question about temperature without knowing the pressure value.

Important Considerations for Interaction Effects

While the plots help you interpret the interaction effects, use a hypothesis test to determine whether the effect is statistically significant. Plots can display non-parallel lines that represent random sample error rather than an actual effect. P-values and hypothesis tests help you sort out the real effects from the noise. For the two examples we assessed, I showed you how the p-values for the interaction terms are statistically significant.

The examples in this chapter are two-way interactions because there are two independent variables in each term (Food*Condiment and Temperature*Pressure). It's equally valid to interpret these effects in two ways. For example, the relationship between:

- Satisfaction and Condiment depends on Food.
- Satisfaction and Food depends on Condiment.

You can have higher-order interactions. For example, a three-way interaction has three variables in the term, such as Food*Condiment*X. In this case, the relationship between Satisfaction and Condiment depends on both Food and X. However, this type of effect is challenging to interpret. In practice, analysts use them infrequently. However, in some models, they might be necessary to provide an adequate fit.

Finally, when you have interaction effects that are statistically significant, do not attempt to interpret the main effects without considering the interaction effects. As the examples show, you will draw the wrong conclusions!

Common Questions about Interaction Effects

Over the years, I've been asked many questions about interaction effects—more about this topic than most. They can be confusing! To finish this chapter, I'll address some of the common questions and concerns.

Interaction effects versus correlation between independent variables

A common misconception is that an interaction effect indicates that the independent variables themselves are correlated. That's not necessarily true. An interaction effect refers to the relationship between each independent variable and the dependent variable. Specifically, an interaction effect indicates that the relationship between an independent variable and the dependent variable changes based on the value of at least one other independent variable. Those independent variables don't need to be correlated for that effect to occur.

Correlated independent variables is another phenomenon, which is called multicollinearity. We'll cover that issue in Chapter 9.

Combinations of significant and insignificant main effects and interaction effects

A common concern occurs while interpreting significant interaction effects when the main effects are not significant. Is that even a valid condition? More generally, how do you interpret the possible combinations of significant/insignificant main effects and significant/insignificant interaction effects?

To understand the answer, let's refresh our memories about each type of effect.

- **Main effect**: The portion of an independent variable's effect on the dependent variable that does not depend on the values of the other variables in the model.
- **Interaction effect**. The portion of an independent variable's effect that does depend on the value of at least one other independent variable in the model.

Furthermore:

The total effect of an independent variable = main effect + interaction effect

When either type of effect is not statistically significant, you have insufficient evidence to conclude that the effect is different from zero. When an effect is not significant, you can zero it out of the above equation.

Let's go through the possibilities! I'll use a model that includes A and B as main effects, and A*B as the interaction effect.

Main effects are significant, but the interaction effect is not significant. In this model, the total effect of A and the total effect of B are contained in the main effects only because the interaction effect is not significant. In others words, all of A's effect is due to the value of A and not influenced by B at all. Conversely, all of B's effect is due to the value of B and not influenced by A at all.

Main effects are significant, and the interaction effect is significant. In this model, the total effect for A and the total effect of B include both main effects and interaction effects. In other words, a portion of A's effect does not depend on the value of B while another portion of A's effect does depend on B. You need to sum the main effect and interaction effect to understand the total effect for either independent variable. For example, the total effect of A = A + A*B and B = B + A*B.

Only the interaction effect is significant. In this model, the total effect of A and the total effect of B both entirely depend on the value of the other variable. Neither variable has a portion of its full effect that is independent of the other variable. In other words, the total effect for either variable is A*B. Yes, this situation is completely okay!

When an interaction effect is significant but an underlying main effect is not significant, do you remove the main effect from the model?

The general rule is to include independent variables as main effects in the model, regardless of their significance, when a statistically significant interaction term contains those variables. This practice allows the model to estimate the interaction effect better.

For example, suppose that A*B is statistically significant but A and/or B is not significant. In this situation, statisticians typically include both A and B in the model regardless of their statistical significance.

The coefficient sign for an interaction term isn't what I expected.

I've been asked multiple times about this issue. This answer gets a little technical, but it's all based on things that we've covered already. The reality is that the coefficient sign for an interaction term really doesn't mean much by itself. After all, the effect of a two-way interaction term is the product of three values—the values of the two variables in the interaction and the coefficient of the interaction term. Depending on the combination of positive and negative values, a negative coefficient can represent a positive effect (i.e., if the product of the variable values is negative). Additionally, while the interaction effect might have, say, a negative sign, the total effect of the main effect and interaction effect might be positive. The interaction effect might make it a little less positive than it would've been otherwise.

Additionally, realize that there is a bit of arbitrariness in the coefficient sign and value for the interaction effect of categorical variables. As discussed in Chapter 3, linear models create indicator variables (0s and 1s) to represent the levels of the categorical variable. Then, the model leaves out the indicator variable for a reference level to avoid perfect multicollinearity. Suppose you have group A and group B. If the model includes the indicator variable for group A, then 1 represents group A, and 0 represents not group A. Or, if the model contains the indicator variable for group B, then 1 represents group B and 0 represents not group B. If you have only two groups A and B, then the 1s and 0s are entirely flipped depending on which indicator variable the model includes.

You can include either indicator variable, and the overall results would be the same. However, the coefficient value will change, and possibly the sign! Changing the reference level affects the output, but the overall interpretation/significance of the results remains the same.

Finally, it's hard to gain much meaning from an interaction coefficient by itself for all these reasons. However, you can see the effect of this term in the interaction plot. As long as the interaction plot makes sense theoretically, I wouldn't worry much about the specific sign or value of the coefficient. I'd only be concerned if the interaction plots didn't make sense for your subject area.

Different statistical software packages estimate different interaction effects for the same dataset.

I've heard that my Minitab output for interaction effects often doesn't match the output from other statistical software. And, SPSS and Stata often don't agree on interaction effects. The reason harkens back to the arbitrariness in the coefficients that I mentioned earlier. These differences occur because the various software packages use different default reference levels when coding the categorical variables. While this can change the coefficients, the p-values and data will tell the same overall story. If you want the output to match between software packages, ensure that they use the same reference levels for your categorical variables.

The lines in my interaction plot don't cross even though the interaction effect is statistically significant?

Many readers have mentioned that they've learned that interaction effects are significant when the lines cross. However, their interaction plots don't display crossed lines for a significant interaction term.

Technically, the hypotheses for the interaction term are the following:

- **Null**: The slopes of the different lines are equal.
- **Alternative**: The slopes of the lines are not equal.

When you have a significant interaction term, you reject the null hypothesis. You have sufficient evidence to conclude that the slopes of the lines are not all equal. If the slopes are not equal, the lines must cross at some point. However, that point might not fall within the range of your data that the interaction plot represents.

The lines in my interaction plot appear to have different slopes, but the interaction term is not significant.

Whether you're assessing differences between means or interaction effects, you might see patterns in your sample data that are just flukes based on the luck of the draw rather than representing a real relationship. Hypothesis tests play a critical role in separating the signal (real effects in the population) from the noise (random sampling error). This protective function helps prevent you from mistaking random error for a real effect.

On interaction plots, random error in your sample can produce lines that appear to have different slopes. However, if the interaction term is not statistically significant, your sample provides insufficient evidence for concluding that it represents a real effect at the population level. In other words, you might be looking at noise in the sample.

Review and Next Steps

Over the previous three chapters, we've covered various types of relationships between the variables in your model.

We've looked at main effects for both continuous and categorical variables. For continuous variables, we also looked at both linear and curvilinear relationships. For main effects, the relationship between an independent and dependent variable does not depend on the value of another variable.

We also looked at interaction effects for both categorical and continuous variables. These relationships do depend on the values of other variables in the model. And, when you have significant interaction effects, it's dangerous interpreting main effects without considering the interaction effect. You don't want to put chocolate sauce on your hot dogs!

You also learned how independent variables can have a portion of their total effects as main effects and interaction effects.

Now you know how to model and interpret these types of relationships. That's great. However, if the model doesn't fit the data, you're barking up the wrong tree! The next chapter shifts gears and covers statistical measures of how well your model fits the data.

CHAPTER 6

Goodness-of-Fit

In this chapter, you will learn about several goodness-of-fit statistics. These measures compare the observed values to the values that the model expects. Smaller discrepancies between the observed and expected values represent a better fit. We'll cover R-squared, adjusted R-squared, predicted R-squared, the standard error of the regression, and the overall F-test of significance.

However, the caveat that applies to coefficients and p-values also applies to these measures. You can't trust them or reliably interpret them until you verify that the residual plots look good!

Assessing the Goodness-of-Fit

First, a quick review of material in chapter 2. Residuals are the distance between the observed value and the fitted value.

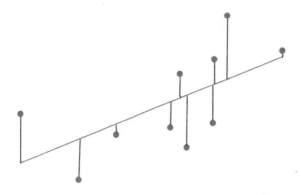

Linear regression identifies the equation that produces the smallest difference between all of the observed values and their fitted values. To be precise, linear regression finds the smallest sum of squared residuals that is possible for the dataset.

Statisticians say that a regression model fits the data well when the differences between the observations and the predicted values are small and unbiased. Unbiased in this context means that the fitted values are not systematically too high or too low anywhere in the observation space.

However, before assessing numeric measures of goodness-of-fit, like R-squared, you should evaluate the residual plots. Residual plots can expose a biased model far more effectively than numeric output by displaying problematic patterns in the residuals. If your model is biased, you cannot trust the results. If your residual plots look good, go ahead and assess your R-squared and other statistics. Chapter 9 covers residual plots.

R-squared

After fitting a linear regression model, you need to determine how well the model fits the data. Does it do a good job of explaining changes in the dependent variable? There are several key goodness-of-fit statistics for regression analysis. First, we'll examine R-squared (R^2), highlight some of its limitations, and discover some surprises.

For instance, small R-squared values are not always a problem, and high R-squared values are not necessarily good!

R-squared evaluates the scatter of the data points around the fitted regression line. It is also called the coefficient of determination, or the coefficient of multiple determination for multiple regression. For the same data set, higher R-squared values represent smaller differences between the observed data and the fitted values.

R-squared is the percentage of the dependent variable variation that a linear model explains.

$$R^2 = \frac{\text{Variance explained by the model}}{\text{Total variance}}$$

R-squared is always between 0 and 100%:

- 0% represents a model that does not explain any of the variation in the response variable around its mean. The mean of the dependent variable predicts the dependent variable as well as the regression model.
- 100% represents a model that explains all of the variation in the response variable around its mean.

Usually, the larger the R^2, the better the regression model fits your observations. However, this guideline has important caveats that I'll discuss in upcoming sections.

Visual Representation of R-squared

To visually demonstrate how R-squared values represent the scatter around the regression line, you can plot the observations with the fitted line that represents the regression equation. Think back to the correlation graphs. Like the correlation coefficient, R-squared measures the strength of the relationship between the set of independent variables and the dependent variables. Stronger relationships indicate lower scatter.

Unlike a correlation coefficient, R-squared does not indicate the direction of the relationship. To make that determination, check the regression coefficients.

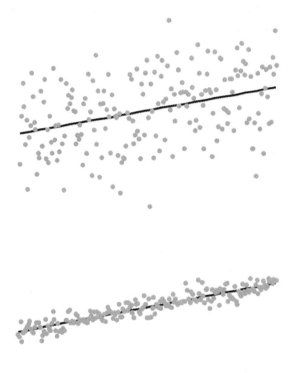

Both graphs use the same scale so you can compare the scatter. The R-squared for the regression model on the top is 15%, and for the model on the bottom it is 85%. When a regression model accounts for more of the variance, the data points are closer to the regression line. For an R^2 of 100%, the fitted values equal the data values and, consequently, all of the observations fall exactly on the regression line. However, in practice, you'll never see a regression model with an R^2 of 100%.

R-squared has Limitations

You cannot use R-squared to determine whether the coefficient estimates and predictions are biased, which is why you must assess the residual plots.

R-squared does not indicate if a regression model provides an adequate fit to your data. A good model can have a low R^2 value. On the other hand, a biased model can have a high R^2 value!

Are Low R-squared Values Always a Problem?

No! Regression models with low R-squared values can be perfectly good models for several reasons.

Some fields of study have an inherently greater amount of unexplainable variation. In these areas, your R^2 values are bound to be lower. For example, studies that try to explain human behavior generally have R^2 values less than 50%. People are just harder to predict than things like physical processes.

Fortunately, if you have a low R-squared value but the independent variables are statistically significant, you can still draw important conclusions about the relationships between the variables. Statistically significant coefficients continue to represent the mean change in the dependent variable given a one-unit shift in the independent variable. Clearly, being able to draw conclusions like this is vital. In a nutshell, if your primary goal is to understand the nature of the relationships in your data, a low R-squared is probably not a problem! I explain this benign aspect of low R-squared values in chapter 11.

There is a scenario where small R-squared values can cause problems. If you need to generate predictions that are relatively precise (narrow prediction intervals), a low R^2 can be a show stopper.

How high does R-squared need to be for the model produce useful predictions? That depends on the precision that you require and the amount of variation present in your data. A high R^2 is necessary for precise predictions, but it is not sufficient by itself, as we'll uncover in the next section.

Are High R-squared Values Always Great?

No! A regression model with a high R-squared value can have a multitude of problems. You probably expect that a high R^2 indicates a good model but examine the following graphs. The fitted line plot models the association between electron mobility and density.

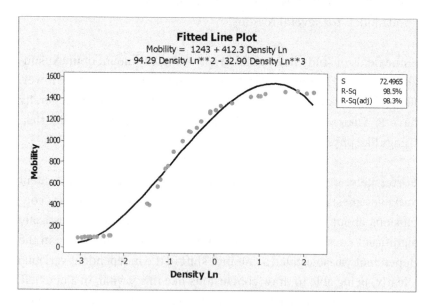

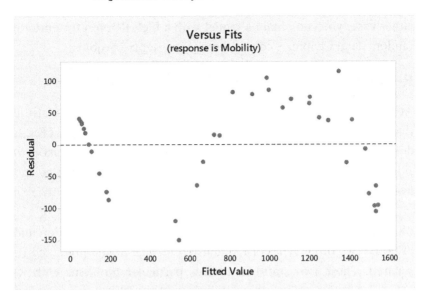

The data in the fitted line plot follow a very low noise relationship, and the R-squared is 98.5%, which seems fantastic. However, the regression line consistently under and over-predicts the data along the curve, which is bias. The Residuals versus Fits plot emphasizes this unwanted pattern. An unbiased model has residuals that are randomly scattered around zero. Non-random residual patterns indicate a bad fit despite a high R^2. Always check your residual plots!

This type of specification bias occurs when your linear model is underspecified. In other words, it is missing significant independent variables, polynomial terms, and interaction terms. To produce random residuals, try adding terms to the model or fitting a nonlinear model.

A variety of other circumstances can artificially inflate your R^2. These reasons include overfitting the model and data mining. Either of these can produce a model that looks like it provides an excellent fit to the data but the results can be entirely deceptive.

An overfit model is one where the model fits the random quirks of the sample. Data mining can take advantage of chance correlations. In either case, you can obtain a model with a high R^2 even for entirely random data! Chapter 8 covers these two potential problems.

R-squared Is Not Always Straightforward

At first glance, R-squared seems like an easy to understand statistic that indicates how well a regression model fits a data set. However, it doesn't tell us the entire story. To get the full picture, you must consider R^2 values in combination with residual plots, other statistics, and in-depth knowledge of the subject area.

I'll continue to explore the limitations of R^2 in the next section and examine two other types of R^2: adjusted R-squared and predicted R-squared. These two statistics address particular problems with R-squared. They provide extra information by which you can assess your regression model's goodness-of-fit.

Adjusted R-Squared and Predicted R-Squared

R-squared tends to reward you for including too many independent variables in a regression model, and it doesn't provide any incentive to stop adding more. Adjusted R-squared and predicted R-squared use different approaches to help you fight that impulse to add too many. The protection that adjusted R-squared and predicted R-squared provide is critical because too many terms in a model can produce results that you can't trust. These statistics help you include the correct number of independent variables in your regression model.

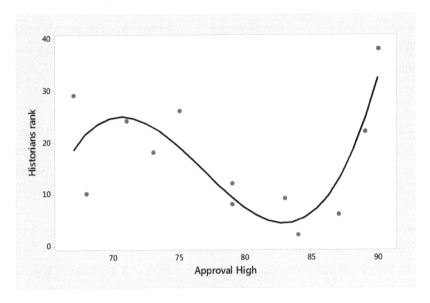

Does this graph display an actual relationship or is it an overfit model? This section shows you how to make this determination.

Multiple regression analysis can seduce you! Yep, you read it here first. It's an incredibly tempting statistical analysis that practically begs you to include additional independent variables in your model. Every time you add a variable, the R-squared increases, which tempts you to add more. Some of the independent variables *will* be statistically significant. Perhaps there is an actual relationship? Or, is it just a chance correlation?

You just pop the variables into the model as they occur to you or just because the data are readily available. Higher-order polynomials curve your regression line any which way you want. But, are you fitting real relationships or just playing connect the dots? Meanwhile, the R-squared increases, mischievously convincing you to include yet more variables!

In the section about interpreting R-squared, I show how evaluating how well a linear regression model fits the data is not as intuitive as you may think. Now, I'll explore reasons why you need to use adjusted R-squared and predicted R-squared to help you specify a good regression model!

Some Problems with R-squared

Previously, I demonstrated that you cannot use R-squared to conclude whether your model is biased. To check for this bias, you need to check your residual plots. Unfortunately, there are yet more problems with R-squared that we need to address.

Problem 1: R-squared increases every time you add an independent variable to the model. The R-squared *never* decreases, not even when it's just a chance correlation between variables. A regression model that contains more independent variables than another model can look like it provides a better fit merely because it contains more variables.

Problem 2: When a model contains an excessive number of independent variables and polynomial terms, it becomes overly customized to fit the peculiarities and random noise in your sample rather than reflecting the entire population. Statisticians call this overfitting the model, and it produces deceptively high R-squared values and a decreased capability for precise predictions.

Fortunately for us, adjusted R-squared and predicted R-squared address both of these problems.

What Is Adjusted R-squared?

Use adjusted R-squared to compare the goodness-of-fit for regression models that contain differing numbers of independent variables.

Let's say you are comparing a model with five independent variables to a model with one variable and the five variable model has a higher R-squared. Is the model with five variables actually a better model, or does it just have more variables? To determine this, just compare the adjusted R-squared values!

The adjusted R-squared adjusts for the number of terms in the model. Importantly, its value increases only when the new term improves the model fit more than expected by chance alone. The adjusted R-squared value actually decreases when the term doesn't improve the model fit by a sufficient amount.

The example below shows how the adjusted R-squared increases up to a point and then decreases. On the other hand, R-squared blithely increases with each and every additional independent variable.

```
Vars  R-sq  R-sq(adj)
  1   72.1       71.0
  2   85.9       84.8
  3   87.4       85.9
  4   89.1       82.3
  5   89.9       80.7
```

In this example, the researchers might want to include only three independent variables in their regression model. While explaining R-squared, I showed how an underspecified model (too few terms) can produce biased estimates.

However, an overspecified model (too many terms) can reduce the model's precision. In other words, when you include too many independent variables, both the coefficient estimates and predicted values can have larger margins of error around them—check those confidence intervals for the coefficients (chapter 3) and prediction intervals (chapter 10)! That's why you don't want to include too many terms in the regression model!

What Is the Predicted R-squared?

Use predicted R-squared to determine how well a regression model makes predictions. This statistic helps you identify cases where the model provides a good fit for the existing data but isn't as good at making predictions. However, even if you aren't using your model to make predictions, predicted R-squared still offers valuable insights about your model.

Statistical software calculates predicted R-squared using the following procedure:

- It removes a data point from the dataset.
- Calculates the regression equation.
- Evaluates how well the model predicts the missing observation.
- And, repeats this for all data points in the dataset.
- Predicted R-squared is a summary statistic of how well the model predicted all of the observations when each one was removed from the dataset for an iteration of the above process.

Predicted R-squared helps you determine whether you are overfitting a regression model. Again, an overfit model includes an excessive number of terms, and it begins to fit the random noise in your sample.

By its very definition, it is not possible to predict random noise. Consequently, if your model fits a lot of random noise, the predicted R-squared value must fall. A predicted R-squared that is distinctly smaller than R-squared is a warning sign that you are overfitting the model. Try reducing the number of terms.

If I had to name my favorite flavor of R-squared, it would be predicted R-squared!

Example of an Overfit Model and Predicted R-squared

You can try this example using this CSV data file: PresidentRanking.

These data come from an analysis I performed that assessed the relationship between the highest approval rating that a U.S. President achieved and their rank by historians. I found no correlation between these variables, as shown in the fitted line plot. It's nearly a perfect example of no relationship because it is a flat line with an R-squared of 0.7%!

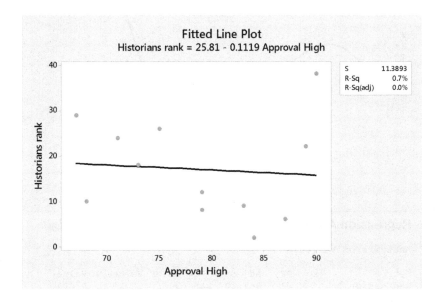

Now, imagine that we are chasing a high R-squared and we fit the model using a cubic term that provides an S-shape.

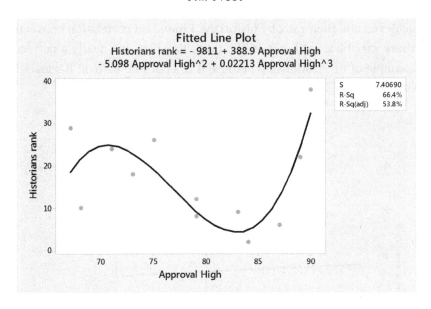

Fitted Line Plot
Historians rank = - 9811 + 388.9 Approval High
- 5.098 Approval High^2 + 0.02213 Approval High^3

S	7.40690
R-Sq	66.4%
R-Sq(adj)	53.8%

Regression Analysis: Historians rank versus Approval High

```
Analysis of Variance

Source               DF    Adj SS   Adj MS  F-Value  P-Value
Regression            3    867.10  289.034     5.27    0.027
  Approval High       1    438.35  438.347     7.99    0.022
  Approval High^2     1    460.23  460.225     8.39    0.020
  Approval High^3     1    481.55  481.552     8.78    0.018
Error                 8    438.90   54.862
  Lack-of-Fit         7    430.90   61.557     7.69    0.271
  Pure Error          1      8.00    8.000
Total                11   1306.00


Model Summary

      S    R-sq  R-sq(adj)  R-sq(pred)
7.40690  66.39%     53.79%       0.00%
```

Amazing! R-squared and adjusted R-squared look great! The coefficients are statistically significant because their p-values are all less than 0.05. I didn't show the residual plots, but they look good as well.

Hold on a moment! We're just twisting the regression line to force it to connect the dots rather than finding an actual relationship. We overfit the model, and the predicted R-squared of 0% gives this away.

If the predicted R-squared is small compared to R-squared, you might be over-fitting the model even if the independent variables are statistically significant.

A Caution about Chasing a High R-squared

All study areas involve a certain amount of variability that you can't explain. If you chase a high R-squared by including an excessive number of variables, you force the model to explain the unexplainable, which is not good. While this approach *can* obtain higher R-squared values, it comes at the cost of misleading regression coefficients, p-values, R-squared, and imprecise predictions.

This problem is known as overfitting and it occurs when your model is too complex and begins to model the random noise. I'll cover this problem in Chapter 8.

Adjusted R-squared and predicted R-square help you resist the urge to add too many independent variables to your model.

- Adjusted R-square compares models with different numbers of variables.
- Predicted R-square can guard against models that are too complicated.

Remember, the great power that comes with multiple regression analysis requires restraint to use it wisely!

Now we'll move on to the standard error of the regression, which is a different type of goodness-of-fit measure.

Standard Error of the Regression vs. R-squared

The standard error of the regression (S) and R-squared are two key goodness-of-fit measures for regression analysis. While R-squared is the most well-known amongst the goodness-of-fit statistics, I think it is a bit over-hyped.

In this section, we'll compare these two statistics and work through a regression example to help make the comparison. I think you'll see that the oft overlooked standard error of the regression can tell you things that the high and mighty R-squared simply can't. At the very least, you'll find that the standard error of the regression is a great tool to add to your statistical toolkit!

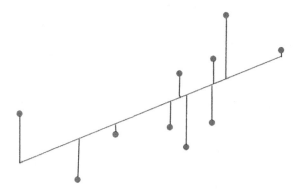

As R-squared increases and S decreases, the data points move closer to the line.

You can find the standard error of the regression, also known as the standard error of the estimate, near R-squared in the goodness-of-fit section of most statistical output. Both of these measures give you a numeric assessment of how well a model fits the sample data. However, there are differences between the two statistics.

- The standard error of the regression provides the absolute measure of the typical distance that the data points fall from the regression line. S is in the units of the dependent variable.
- R-squared provides the relative measure of the percentage of the dependent variable variance that the model explains. R-squared can range from 0 to 100%.

An analogy makes the difference very clear. Suppose we're talking about how fast a car is traveling.

R-squared is equivalent to saying that the car went 80% faster. That sounds a lot faster! However, it makes a huge difference whether the initial speed was 20 MPH or 90 MPH. The *increased* velocity based on the percentage can be either 16 MPH or 72 MPH, respectively. One is lame, and the other is very impressive. If you need to know exactly how much faster, the relative measure just isn't going to tell you.

The standard error of the regression is equivalent to telling you directly how many MPH faster the car is traveling. The car went 72 MPH faster. Now that's impressive!

Let's move on to how we can use these two goodness-of-fits measures in regression analysis.

Standard Error of the Regression and R-squared in Practice

In my view, the standard error of the regression has several advantages. S tells you straight up how precise the model's predictions are using the units of the dependent variable. This statistic indicates how far the data points are from the regression line on average. You want lower values of S because it signifies that the distances between the data points and the fitted values are smaller. S is also valid for both linear and nonlinear regression models. This fact is convenient if you need to compare the fit between both types of models.

For R-squared, you want the regression model to explain higher percentages of the variance. Higher R-squared values indicate that the data points are closer to the fitted values. While higher R-squared values are good, they don't tell you how far the data points are from the regression line. Additionally, R-squared is valid for only linear models. You can't use R-squared to compare a linear model to a nonlinear model.

Note: Linear models can use polynomials to model curvature. I'm using the term linear to refer to models that are linear in the parameters.

Example Regression Model: BMI and Body Fat Percentage

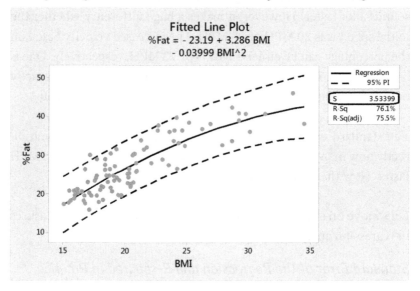

This regression model describes the relationship between body mass index (BMI) and body fat percentage in middle school girls. It's a linear model that uses a polynomial term to model the curvature. The fitted line plot indicates that the standard error of the regression is 3.53399% body fat. The interpretation of this S is that the standard distance between the observations and the regression line is ~3.5% body fat. (Note: S is a percentage in this example only because the original data are in percentages. S is always in the same units as the original dependent variable.)

S measures the precision of the model's predictions. Consequently, we can use S to obtain a rough estimate of the 95% prediction interval. About 95% of the data points are within a range that extends from +/- 2 * standard error of the regression from the fitted line.

For the regression example, approximately 95% of the data points lie between the regression line and +/- 7% body fat.

The R-squared is 76.1%.

I Often Prefer the Standard Error of the Regression

R-squared is a percentage, which seems easy to understand. However, I often appreciate the standard error of the regression a bit more. I value the concrete insight provided by using the original units of the dependent variable. If I'm using the regression model to produce predictions, S tells me at a glance if the model is sufficiently precise.

On the other hand, R-squared doesn't have any units, and it feels more ambiguous than S. If all we know is that R-squared is 76.1%, we don't know how wrong the model is on average. You do need a high R-squared to produce precise predictions, but you don't know how high it must be exactly. It's impossible to use R-squared to evaluate the precision of the predictions.

To demonstrate this, we'll look at the regression example. Let's assume that our predictions must be within +/- 5% of the actual values to be useful. If we know only that R-squared is 76.1%, can we determine whether our model is sufficiently precise? No, you can't tell using R-squared.

However, you *can* use the standard error of the regression. For our model to have the required precision, S must be less than 2.5% because 2.5 * 2 = 5. In an instant, we know that our S (~3.5) is too large. We need a more precise model. Thanks S!

While I really like the standard error of the regression, you can, of course, consider both goodness-of-fit measures simultaneously. This is the statistical equivalent of having your caking and eating it!

We'll switch gears again and look at yet another statistic that assesses the fit of the model.

The F-test of Overall Significance

The F-test of overall significance indicates whether your linear regression model provides a better fit to the data than a model that contains no independent variables. In this section, you will learn how the F-test of overall significance fits in with R-squared. R-squared tells you how well your model fits the data, and the F-test is related to it.

An F-test is a type of statistical test that is very flexible. You can use them in a wide variety of settings. F-tests can evaluate multiple model terms simultaneously, which allows them to compare the fits of different linear models. In contrast, t-tests can evaluate just one term at a time.

To calculate the F-test of overall significance, your statistical software includes the proper terms in the two models that it compares. The overall F-test compares the model that you specify to the model with no independent variables, which is also known as an intercept-only model.

The F-test for overall significance has the following two hypotheses:

- The null hypothesis states that the model with no independent variables fits the data as well as your model.
- The alternative hypothesis says that your model fits the data better than the intercept-only model.

In statistical output, you can find the overall F-test in the ANOVA table.

Analysis of Variance

Source	DF	Adj SS	Adj MS	F-Value	P-Value
Regression	3	12833.9	4278.0	57.87	0.000
East	1	226.3	226.3	3.06	0.092
South	1	2255.1	2255.1	30.51	0.000
North	1	12330.6	12330.6	166.80	0.000
Error	25	1848.1	73.9		
Total	28	14681.9			

Compare the p-value for the F-test to your significance level. If the p-value is less than the significance level, your sample data provide sufficient evidence to conclude that your regression model fits the data better than the model with no independent variables.

This finding is good news because it means that the independent variables in your model improve the fit!

Generally speaking, if none of your independent variables are statistically significant, the overall F-test is also not statistically significant. Occasionally, the t-tests for coefficients and the overall F-test can produce conflicting results. This disagreement can occur because the F-test of overall significance assesses all of the coefficients jointly whereas the t-test for each coefficient examines them individually. For example, the overall F-test can find that the coefficients are significant *jointly* while the t-tests can fail to find significance *individually*.

These conflicting test results can be hard to understand, but think about it this way. The F-test sums the predictive power of all independent variables and determines that it is unlikely that *all* of the coefficients equal zero. However, it's possible that each variable isn't predictive enough on its own to be statistically significant. In other words, your sample provides sufficient evidence to conclude that your model is significant, but not enough to conclude that any individual variable is significant.

Additional Ways to Interpret the F-test of Overall Significance

If you have a statistically significant overall F-test, you can draw several other conclusions.

For the model with no independent variables, the intercept-only model, all of the model's predictions equal the mean of the dependent variable. Consequently, if the overall F-test is statistically significant, your model's predictions are an improvement over using the mean.

R-squared measures the strength of the relationship between your model and the dependent variable. However, it is not a formal test for the relationship. The F-test of overall significance is the hypothesis test for this relationship. If the overall F-test is significant, you can conclude that R-squared does not equal zero, and the correlation between the model and dependent variable is statistically significant. On the other hand, if the overall F-test is not significant, your sample does not provide strong enough evidence for concluding that R-squared is greater than zero in the population.

It's fabulous if your regression model is statistically significant! However, remember the lessons from the R-squared section, the numbers tell an incomplete story. Check your residual plots to determine whether the results are trustworthy!

Review and Next Steps

In this chapter, we revisited R-squared. While it appears to be a straight-forward goodness-of-fit measure, it's not entirely intuitive. Low R-squared values are not inherently bad, and high R-squared values are not intrinsically good. You also learned how R-squared and chasing a high R-squared have problems. R-squared can entice you to add too many variables to the model. If you go past the natural amount of explainable variability, you can't trust the results. Fortunately, adjusted R-squared and predicted R-squared can help you avoid these problems.

I also covered the standard error of the regression (S), which is a statistic that I particularly like. It represents how wrong your model is typically using the natural units of the dependent variable.

Finally, you learned how the overall F-test is a hypothesis test that determines whether the set of variables in your model provides a significantly better fit compared to a model that contains no independent variables. It's also a hypothesis test that determines whether the *population* R-squared is greater than zero.

Up to this point, you've learned how regression can help you, how it fits the best line, how to interpret a variety of effects, how to fit curves in your data, and how to use several statistical measures to determine how well your model fits the data. Now, we can move on to the process of deciding which independent variables to include in your model. As I mentioned previously, model specification is an iterative process. You'll use the statistics we've covered, along with the residual plots that we'll cover later, to help you specify the correct model, assess it, and make changes.

CHAPTER 7

Specify Your Model

Model specification is the process of determining which independent variables belong in the model and whether modeling curvature and interaction effects are appropriate. Which independent variables do you include and exclude from a regression equation?

How do you choose the best regression model? The world is complicated and trying to explain it with a small sample doesn't help. In this chapter, I'll show you how to select the correct model. I'll cover statistical methods, difficulties that can arise, and provide practical suggestions for selecting your model. Often, the variable selection process is a mixture of statistics, theory, and practical knowledge.

The need for model selection often begins when a researcher wants to mathematically define the relationship between independent variables and the dependent variable. Typically, investigators measure many variables but include only some in the model. Analysts try to exclude independent variables that are not related and include only those that have an actual relationship with the dependent variable. During the specification process, the analysts typically try different combinations of variables and various forms of the model. For example, they can try different terms that explain interactions between variables and curvature in the data.

The analysts need to reach a Goldilocks balance by including the correct number of independent variables in the regression equation.

- o **Too few**: Underspecified models tend to be biased.
- o **Too many**: Overspecified models tend to be less precise.
- o **Just right**: Models with the correct terms are not biased and are the most precise.

If your study wants to test a particular relationship, your regression equation should contain the independent variables that you are explicitly testing along with other variables that affect the dependent variable. This process allows your regression model to assess your study's research questions while controlling for other variables that can influence the dependent variable.

For example, I was on a research project that wanted to determine whether a particular exercise intervention increased bone mineral density in preteen girls as a way to reduce their risk of osteoporosis later in life. My regression model for this study included the exercise intervention along with other independent variables that influence bone density. These additional variables include general activity levels, nutrition, and various health and body measurements. This model could estimate the effect of the intervention while controlling for the other relevant variables.

The Importance of Graphing Your Data

When you start working with a dataset to build a regression model, the first thing you should do is graph your data. At a glance, you'll learn a lot about your data and the relationships between variables. For regression analysis, where most data are continuous, scatterplots are crucial. Scatterplots will show you whether there are positive or negative relationships and if they are linear or curvilinear. When some relationships are curved, the shape of the curve in the scatterplot might provide ideas about how to model it. You can also calculate the correlations between the candidate independent variables and the dependent variable. Significant correlations suggest that you should consider including those variables in the model.

Personally, I prefer using scatterplots over correlations. Remember the U-shaped scatterplot in chapter 1 that had a correlation near zero? If you went by that correlation alone, you might not consider including that variable in the model. However, using the scatterplot, you'd realize there is a relationship between those two variables, and that you need to include a polynomial term to model the curvature! I'll say this over and over, graphs bring your data to life in ways that numbers don't. Statistics are best when you can combine graphs and numeric statistical measures to paint the full picture.

You can include categorical variables in scatterplots to determine whether those variables play a role. Alternatively, you can graph your dependent variable by groups using boxplots or individual value plots. I presented an example boxplot in chapter 3 and showed how you can test that relationship by including a categorical variable in the model.

If you're working on a multiple regression model, you can use a scatterplot matrix to display numerous relationships at the same time.

In the matrix plot, the analysts are considering using the body measurements of bears to predict their weights. Weight is the dependent variable while the other measurements are the independent variables. The idea behind the study is that it might be easier to estimate the bears' weights by using body measurements rather than actually weighing the bear!

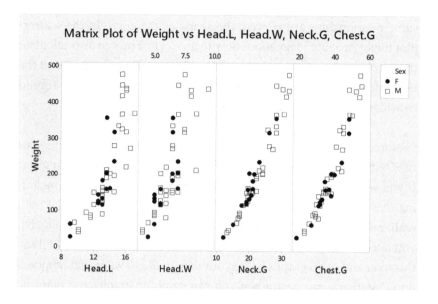

The scatterplot matrix shows how each body measurement variable relates to weight. Notice how the relationships between the potential independent variables and the dependent variable are all positive. That makes sense because a larger bear should be more massive. Additionally, the two head measurements appear to have a curvilinear relationship with weight.

I included the bear's gender as a grouping variable. If the scatterplots had shown a shift in weights based on gender, it would have suggested including Gender in the model as a categorical variable. However, as the graphs show, there is no shift in weights by gender. The two genders follow the same relationship.

These four independent variables are good candidates for inclusion in the model. The analysts will likely need to fit the curvature for several variables.

Statistical Methods for Model Specification

You can use statistical assessments during the model specification process. Various metrics and algorithms can help you determine which independent variables to include in your regression equation. Let's review some standard approaches to model selection, but please refer to the previous chapters for more details about the statistics.

Adjusted R-squared and Predicted R-squared

Typically, you want to select models that have larger adjusted and predicted R-squared values. These statistics can help you avoid the fundamental problem with regular R-squared—it *always* increases when you add an independent variable. This property tempts you into specifying a model that is too complex, which can produce misleading results.

- Adjusted R-squared increases only when a new variable improves the model by more than chance. Low-quality variables can cause it to decrease.
- Predicted R-squared is a cross-validation method that can also decrease. Cross-validation partitions your data to determine whether the model is generalizable outside of your dataset.

Mallows' Cp

Mallows' Cp helps you choose between multiple regression models by striking a balance between precision and bias. You want to include a sufficient number of independent variables to eliminate bias but not too many to reduce precision. This balance changes with the number of independent variables in the model. Mallows' Cp compares the precision and bias of the full model to models with a subset of the predictors.

Typically, you want Mallows' Cp to be small and close to the number of variables in the model plus the constant. A Mallows' Cp value that meets these criteria suggests that the coefficient estimates are both relatively precise (small variance) and unbiased. Biased models have larger values of Mallows' Cp. We'll revisit Mallows' Cp in the context of stepwise and best subsets regression.

P-values for the independent variables

In regression, p-values less than the significance level indicate that the term is statistically significant. When a variable is not significant, consider removing it from the model. "Reducing the model" is the process of including all candidate variables in the model, and then repeatedly removing the single term with the highest non-significant p-value until your model contains only significant terms.

Stepwise regression and Best subsets regression

These two automated model selection procedures are algorithms that pick the variables to include in your regression equation. These automated methods can be helpful when you have many independent variables, and you need some help in the investigative stages of the variable selection process. These procedures can provide the Mallows' Cp statistic, which helps you balance the tradeoff between precision and bias. You'll learn about these selection procedures later in this chapter.

Real-World Complications

The good news is that there are statistical methods that can help you with model specification. Unfortunately, there are a variety of complications that can arise. Fear not! I'll provide some practical advice! I cover many of these issues in other chapters as indicated.

- Your best model is only as good as the data you collect. Specification of the correct model depends on you measuring the proper variables. In fact, when you omit important variables from the model, the estimates for the variables that you include can be biased. This condition is known as omitted variable bias, which I cover in the next section.
- The sample you collect can be unusual, either by luck or methodology. False discoveries and false negatives are inevitable when you work with samples.

- Multicollinearity occurs when independent variables in a regression equation are correlated. When multicollinearity is present, small changes in the equation can produce dramatic changes in coefficients and p-values. It can also reduce statistical significance in variables that are relevant. For these reasons, multicollinearity makes model selection challenging. (Chapter 9).
- If you fit many models during the model selection process, you will find variables that appear to be statistically significant, but they are correlated only by chance. This problem occurs because all hypothesis tests have a false discovery rate. This type of data mining can make even random data appear to have significant relationships! I show you how this happens in Chapter 8.
- P-values, adjusted R-squared, predicted R-squared, and Mallows' Cp can point to different regression equations. Sometimes there is not a clear answer.
- Stepwise regression and best subsets regression are automated model selection procedures that can help you in the early stages of model specification. However, studies show that these tools can get close to the right answer but they usually don't specify the correct model. You'll learn how these methods work later in this chapter.

Practical Recommendations

Model specification is as much a science as it is an art. Statistical methods can help, but, ultimately, you'll need to place a high weight on theory and other considerations. I'll cover these topics in greater detail later in the book, but here's an overview of the issues at hand.

Theory

The best practice is to review the literature to develop a theoretical understanding of the relevant independent variables, their relationships with the dependent variable, and the expected coefficient signs and effect magnitudes before you begin collecting data. Building your knowledge helps you collect the correct data in the first place and it helps you specify the best regression equation without resorting to data mining.

Specification should not be based only on statistical measures. In fact, the foundation of your model selection process should depend largely on theoretical concerns. Be sure to determine whether your statistical results match theory and, if necessary, make adjustments. For example, if theory suggests that an independent variable is important, you might include it in the regression equation even when its p-value is not significant. If a coefficient sign is the opposite of theory, investigate and either modify the model or explain the inconsistency.

Simplicity

Analysts often think that complex problems require complicated regression equations. However, studies reveal that simplification usually produces more precise models. When you have several models with similar predictive power, choose the simplest because it is the most likely to be the best model. (Zellner, Keuzenkamp, & McAleer, 2009)

Start simple and then add complexity only when it is actually needed. As you make a model more complex, it becomes more likely that you are tailoring it to fit the quirks in your particular dataset rather than actual relationships in the population. This overfitting reduces generalizability and can produce results that you can't trust.

To avoid overly complex models, don't chase a high R-squared mindlessly. Confirm that additional complexity aligns with theory and produces narrower confidence intervals for the coefficients and narrower prediction intervals. Check other measures, such as predicted R-squared, which can alert you to overfitting.

Residual Plots

During the specification process, check the residual plots. Residuals plots are an easy way to avoid biased models and can help you make adjustments. For instance, residual plots display patterns when an underspecified regression equation is biased, which can indicate the need to model curvature. The simplest model that creates random residuals is a great contender for being reasonably precise and unbiased.

Ultimately, statistical measures can't tell you which regression equation is best. They just don't understand the fundamentals of the subject-area. Your expertise is always a vital part of the model specification process!

In short, we want simple models that you choose based on theory. It's tempting to try many combinations of variables to find the best model, but that's not the best approach. In chapter 8, you'll learn how using a shotgun, data dredging approach can cause problems!

Omitted Variable Bias

The previous section primarily focuses on determining which variables you should include in your model. Now, I'm going to flip that on its head and show you how to determine which variables you should not exclude. Yeah, I know, after processing that double-negative, it sounds exactly the same. It's definitely related, but it's critical to understand the consequences of omitting an important variable from the model. That's the focus of this section.

Omitted variable bias occurs when a regression model leaves out relevant independent variables, which are known as confounding variables. This condition forces the model to attribute the effects of omitted variables to variables that are in the model, which biases the coefficient estimates.

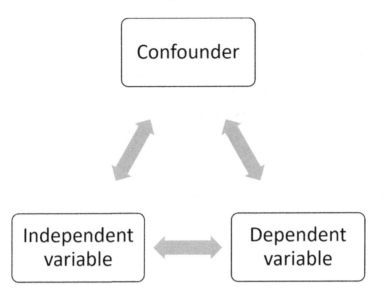

This problem occurs because your linear regression model is specified incorrectly—either because the confounding variables are unknown or because the data do not exist. If this bias affects your model, it is a severe condition because you can't trust your results.

In this section, you'll learn about this type of bias, how it occurs, and how to detect and correct it.

What Are the Effects of Omitted Variable Bias?

Omitting confounding variables from your regression model can bias the coefficient estimates. What does that mean exactly? When you're assessing the regression coefficients in the statistical output, this bias can produce the following problems:

- Overestimate the strength of an effect.
- Underestimate the strength of an effect.
- Change the sign of an effect.
- Mask an effect that actually exists.

You don't want any of these problems to affect your regression results!

Synonyms for Confounding Variables and Omitted Variable Bias

In the context of regression analysis, there are various synonyms for omitted variables and the bias they can cause. Analysts often refer to omitted variables that cause bias as confounding variables, confounders, and lurking variables. These are important variables that the statistical model does not include and, therefore, cannot control. Additionally, they call the bias itself omitted variable bias, spurious effects, and spurious relationships. I'll use these terms interchangeably.

What Conditions Cause Omitted Variable Bias?

How does this bias occur? How can variables you leave out of the model affect the variables that you include in the model? At first glance, this problem might not make sense.

For omitted variable bias to occur, the following two conditions must exist:

- The omitted variable must correlate with the dependent variable.
- The omitted variable must correlate with at least one independent variable that is in the regression model.

The diagram below illustrates these two conditions. There must be non-zero correlations (r) on all three sides of the triangle.

Independent Dependent

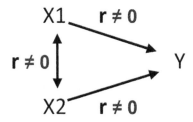

This correlation structure causes confounding variables that are not in the model to bias the estimates that appear in your regression results. For example, in the previous diagram, removing either X variable from the model will bias the other X variable.

The amount of bias depends on the strength of these correlations. Strong correlations produce greater bias. If the relationships are weak, the bias might not be severe. And, if the omitted variable is not correlated with another independent variable at all, excluding it does not produce bias.

Finally, if you're performing a randomized experiment, omitted variable bias is less likely to be a problem. Randomized studies minimize the effects of confounding variables by equally distributing them across the treatment groups. Omitted variable bias tends to occur in observational studies.

I'll explain how confounding variables can bias the results using two approaches. First, I'll work through an example and describe how the omitted variable forces the model to attribute the effects of the excluded variable to the one in the model. Then, I'll go into a more statistical explanation that details the correlation structure, residuals, and an assumption violation. Explaining confounding variables using both approaches will give you a solid grasp of how the bias occurs.

Practical Example of How Confounding Variables Can Produce Bias

I used to work in a biomechanics lab. One study assessed the effects of physical activity on bone density. We measured various characteristics including the subjects' activity levels, their weights, and bone densities among many others. Theories about how our bodies build bone suggest that there should be a positive correlation between activity level and bone density. In other words, higher activity produces greater bone density.

Early in the study, I wanted to validate our initial data quickly by using simple regression analysis to determine whether there is a relationship between activity and bone density. If our data were valid, there should be a positive relationship. To my great surprise, there was no relationship at all!

What was happening? The theory is well established in the field. Maybe our data was messed up somehow? Long story short, thanks to a confounding variable, the model was exhibiting omitted variable bias.

To perform the quick assessment, I included activity level as the only independent variable, but it turns out there is another variable that correlates with both activity and bone density—the subject's weight.

After including weight in the regression model, along with activity, the results indicated that both activity and weight are statistically significant and have positive correlations with bone density. The diagram below shows the signs of the correlations between the variables.

Independent   **Dependent**

Activity ___ +

－ ↕

Weight ⟋ +   Bone density

How the Omitted Confounding Variable Hid the Relationship

Right away we see that these conditions can produce omitted variable bias because all three sides of the triangle have non-zero correlations. Let's find out how leaving weight out of the model masked the relationship between activity and bone density.

Subjects who are more active tend to have higher bone density. Additionally, subjects who weigh more also tend to have higher bone density. However, there is a negative correlation between activity and weight. More active subjects tend to weigh less.

This correlation structure produces two opposing effects of activity. More active subjects get a bone density boost. However, they also tend to weigh less, which reduces bone density.

When I fit a regression model with only activity, the model had to attribute both opposing effects to activity alone. Hence, the zero correlation. However, when I fit the model with both activity and weight, it could assign the opposing effects to each variable separately.

For this example, when I omitted weight from the model, it produced a negative bias because the model underestimated the effect of activity. The results said there is no correlation when there is, in fact, a positive correlation.

Correlations, Residuals, and OLS Assumptions

Let's look at this from another angle that involves the residuals and an assumption. When you satisfy the ordinary least squares (OLS) assumptions, the Gauss-Markov theorem states that your estimates will be unbiased and have minimum variance. We'll cover all of these topics in more detail in Chapter 9.

Omitted variable bias occurs because the residuals violate one of the assumptions. To see how this works, you need to follow a chain of events.

Suppose you have a regression model with two significant independent variables, X1 and X2. These independent variables correlate with each other and the dependent variable—which are the requirements for omitted variable bias.

Now, imagine that we take variable X2 out of the model. It is the confounding variable. Here's what happens:

1. The model fits the data less well because we've removed a significant explanatory variable. Consequently, the gap between the observed values and the fitted values increases. These gaps are the residuals.
2. The degree to which each residual increases depends on the relationship between X2 and the dependent variable. Consequently, the residuals correlate with X2.
3. X1 correlates with X2, and X2 correlates with the residuals. Ergo, variable X1 correlates with the residuals.
4. Hence, this condition violates the ordinary least squares assumption that independent variables in the model do not correlate with the residuals. Violations of this assumption produce biased estimates.

This explanation serves a purpose soon!

The important takeaway here is that leaving out an important variable not only reduces the goodness-of-fit (larger residuals), but it can also bias the coefficient estimates.

Predicting the Direction of Omitted Variable Bias

We can use correlation structures, like the one in the example, to predict the direction of bias that occurs when the model omits a confounding variable. The direction depends on both the correlation between the included and omitted independent variables and the correlation between the included independent variable and the dependent variable. The table summarizes these relationships and the direction of bias.

	Included & Omitted: Negative Correlation	Included & Omitted: Positive Correlation
Included and Dependent: Negative Correlation	Positive bias: Coefficient is overestimated.	Negative bias: Coefficient is underestimated.
Included and Dependent: Positive Correlation	Negative bias: Coefficient is underestimated.	Positive bias: Coefficient is overestimated.

Let's apply this table to the bone density example. The included (Activity) and omitted confounding variable (Weight) have a negative correlation, so we need to use the middle column. The included variable (Weight) and the dependent variable (Bone Density) have a positive relationship, which corresponds to the bottom row. At the intersection of the middle column and bottom row, the table indicates that we can expect a negative bias, which matches our results.

Suppose we hadn't collected weight and were unable to include it in the model. In that case, we can use this table, along with the hypothesized relationships, to predict the direction of the omitted variable bias. However, because I had collected the weight data, I was able to include Weight in the model and observe how it removed the bias.

How to Detect Omitted Variable Bias and Identify Confounding Variables

You saw one method of detecting omitted variable bias in this section. If you include different combinations of independent variables in the model, and you see the coefficients changing, you're watching omitted variable bias in action!

In the previous example, I started with a regression model that has activity as the lone independent variable and bone density as the dependent variable. After adding weight to the model, the correlation changed from zero to positive.

However, if we don't have the data, it can be harder to detect omitted variable bias. If my study hadn't collected the weight data, the answer would not be as clear.

I presented a clue earlier in this section. We know that for omitted variable bias to exist, an independent variable must correlate with the residuals. Consequently, we can plot the residuals by the variables in our model. If we see a relationship in the plot, rather than random scatter, it both tells us that there is a problem and points us towards the solution. We know which independent variable correlates with the confounding variable. That knowledge might help you track down the problem.

Another step is to carefully consider theory and other studies. Ask yourself several questions:

Do the coefficient estimates match the theoretical signs and magnitudes? If not, you need to investigate. That was my first tip-off!

Can you think of confounding variables that you didn't measure that are likely to correlate with both the dependent variable and at least one independent variable? Reviewing the literature, consulting experts, and brainstorming sessions can shed light on this possibility.

Obstacles to Correcting Omitted Variable Bias

Again, you've already seen the best correction possible—including the variable in the model! Including confounding variables in a regression model allows the analysis to control for them and prevent the spurious effects that the omitted variables would have caused otherwise. Theoretically, you should include all independent variables that have a relationship with the dependent variable. That's easier said than done because this approach produces real-world problems.

For starters, you might need to collect data on many more character-istics than is feasible. Additionally, some of these characteristics might be very difficult or even impossible to measure. Suppose you fit a model for salary that includes experience and education. Ability might also be a significant variable, but one that is much harder to measure in some fields.

Furthermore, as you include more variables in the model, the number of observations must increase to avoid overfitting the model, which can also produce unreliable results. Measuring more characteristics and gathering a larger sample size can be an expensive proposition!

Because the bias occurs when the confounding variables correlate with independent variables, including these confounders invariably introduces multicollinearity into your model. Multicollinearity causes its own problems including unstable coefficient estimates, lower sta-tistical power, and less precise estimates.

It's important to note a tradeoff that might occur between precision and bias. As you include the formerly omitted variables, you lessen the bias, but the increased multicollinearity can potentially reduce the precision of the estimates.

It's a balancing act! Let's get into some practical recommendations.

Recommendations for Addressing Confounding Variables and Omitted Variable Bias

Before you begin your study, arm yourself with all the possible back-ground information you can gather. Research the study area, review the literature, and consult with experts. This process enables you to identify and measure the crucial variables that you should include in your model. It helps you avoid the problem in the first place. Just im-agine if you collect all your data and then realize that you didn't meas-ure a critical variable. That's an expensive mistake!

After the analysis, this background information can help you identify potential bias, and, if necessary, track down the solution.

Check those residual plots! Sometimes you might not be sure whether bias exists, but the plots can clearly display the hallmarks of confounding variables.

Recognize that omitted variable bias lessens as the degree of correlations decrease. It might not always be a significant problem. Understanding the relationships between the variables helps you make this determination.

Remember that a tradeoff between bias and the precision of the estimates might occur. As you add confounding variables to reduce the bias, keep an eye on the precision of the estimates. To track the precision, check the confidence intervals of the coefficient estimates. If the intervals become wider, the estimates are less precise. In the end, you might accept a little bias if it significantly improves precision.

What to Do When Including Confounding Variables is Impossible

If you absolutely cannot include an important variable and it causes omitted variable bias, consider using a proxy variable. Typically, proxy variables are easy to measure, and analysts use them instead of variables that are either impossible or difficult to measure. The proxy variable can be a characteristic that is not of any great importance itself, but has a good correlation with the confounding variable.

These variables allow you to include some of the information in your model that would not otherwise be possible, and, thereby, reduce omitted variable bias. For example, if it is crucial to include historical climate data in your model, but those data do not exist, you might include tree ring widths instead.

Finally, if you can't correct omitted variable bias using any method, you can at least predict the direction of bias for your estimates. After identifying confounding variable candidates, you can estimate their theoretical correlations with the relevant variables and predict the direction of the bias—as we did with the bone density example.

If you aren't careful, the hidden hazards of confounding variables and omitted variable bias can completely flip the results of your regression analysis! It's easy to get stuck on determining which of your set of candidate variables to include that you forget to consider which variables you might be excluding without even realizing it!

Automated Variable Selection Procedures

Previously, we went through both the art and science of specifying your model. How to decide which variables to include or exclude, and how to help ensure you weren't leaving out any important variables. While I strongly recommend using theory and knowledge to guide you, there are automated procedures that can help you identify candidate variables early in the process. I'm not a big fan of these automated procedures because they use only statistical measures and no subject-area knowledge. However, most statistical software includes these analyses. You should know how they work and their limitations.

Automatic variable selection procedures are algorithms that pick the variables to include in your regression model. Stepwise regression and Best Subsets regression are two of the more common variable selection methods. Let's see how well they work and determine whether one provides better results.

These automatic procedures can help when you have many independent variables, and you need assistance in the investigative stages of the variable selection process. You could specify many models with different combinations of independent variables, or you can have your statistical software do this for you.

These procedures are especially useful when theory and experience provide only a vague sense of which variables you should include in the model. However, if theory and expertise are strong guides, it's generally better to follow them than to use an automated procedure. Additionally, if you use one of these procedures, you should consider it as only the first step of the model selection process.

Here are my objectives for this section. I will:

- Show how stepwise regression and best subsets regression work differently.
- Use both procedures on one example dataset to compare their results.
- Explore whether one procedure is better.
- Examine the factors that affect a method's ability to choose the correct model.

How Stepwise Regression Works

As the name stepwise regression suggests, this procedure selects variables in a step-by-step manner. This procedure begins with a set of candidate independent variables and then adds or removes independent variables one at a time using the variable's statistical significance. Stepwise either adds the most significant variable or removes the least significant variable. It does not consider all possible models, and it produces a single regression model when the algorithm ends.

Typically, you can control the specifics of the stepwise procedure. For example, you can specify whether it can only add variables, only remove variables, or both. You can also set the significance level for including and excluding the independent variables.

How Best Subsets Regression Works

Best subsets regression is also known as "all possible regressions" and "all possible models." Again, the name of the procedure indicates how it works. Unlike stepwise, best subsets regression fits all possible models based on the independent variables that you specify.

The number of models that this procedure fits multiplies quickly. If you have 10 independent variables, it fits 1024 models. However, if you have 20 variables, it fits 1,048,576 models! Best subsets regression fits 2^P models, where P is the number of predictors in the dataset.

After fitting all of the models, best subsets regression then displays the best fitting models with one independent variable, two variables, three variables, and so on. Usually, either adjusted R-squared or Mallows' Cp is the criterion for picking the best fitting models for this process.

The procedure displays the best fitting models of different sizes up to the full model. You need to compare the models to determine which one is the best. In some cases, it is not clear which model is the best, and you'll need to use your judgment.

Comparing Stepwise to Best Subsets Regression

While both automatic variable selection procedures assess the full set of candidate independent variables that you specify, the end results can be different. Stepwise regression does not fit all models but instead assesses the statistical significance of the variables one at a time and arrives at a single model. Best subsets regression fits all possible models and displays some of the best candidates based on adjusted R-squared or Mallows' Cp.

The single model that stepwise regression produces can be simpler for the analyst. However, best subsets regression presents more information that is potentially valuable.

Enough talk about how these procedures work. Let's see them in action!

Using Stepwise and Best Subsets on the Same Dataset

Our example scenario models a manufacturing process. We'll determine whether the production conditions are related to the strength of a product. If you want to try this yourself, use the CSV data file: ProductStrength.

For both variable selection procedures, we'll use the same independent and dependent variables.

- **Dependent variable:** Strength
- **Independent variables:** Temperature, Pressure, Rate, Concentration, Time

Example of Stepwise Regression

Let's use stepwise regression to pick the variables for our model. I'll use the stepwise method that allows the procedure to both add and remove independent variables as needed. The output displays the steps up to the fourth and final step.

```
Stepwise Selection of Terms

Candidate terms: Temperature, Pressure, Rate, Concentration, Time

                ----Step 1----   ----Step 2----   ----Step 3----   ----Step 4----
                  Coef      P      Coef      P      Coef      P      Coef      P
Constant         607.1            483.7            389.2            270.2
Concentration   -21.40   0.000   -24.22   0.000   -24.13   0.000   -21.12   0.000
Rate                              4.796   0.000    5.318   0.000    5.339   0.000
Pressure                                           2.12    0.092    2.95    0.025
Temperature                                                         0.0516  0.067

S                12.3277          8.93207          8.59782          8.16981
R-sq             72.05%           85.87%           87.41%           89.09%
R-sq(adj)        71.02%           84.78%           85.90%           87.27%
R-sq(pred)       66.93%           81.36%           78.96%           80.61%
Mallows' Cp      38.49            9.10             7.60             5.79

α to enter = 0.15, α to remove = 0.15
```

For our example data, the stepwise procedure added a variable in each step. The process stopped when there were no variables it could add or remove from the model. The final column displays the model that the procedure produced.

The four independent variables in our model are Concentration, Rate, Pressure, and Temperature. This model has an R-squared of 89.09% and the highest adjusted R-squared. You also want Mallows' Cp to be close to the number of independent variables plus one (for the constant). Mallows' Cp for the final model is closer to the ideal value than the other models. It all looks good!

Example of Best Subsets Regression

Next, I'll perform best subsets regression on the same dataset. This procedure fits all possible models using our five independent variables. That means it fit $2^5 = 32$ models. Each horizontal line represents a different model. By default, this statistical software package displays the top two models for each number of independent variables that are in the model. X's indicate the independent variables that are in each model.

Best Subsets Regression: Strength versus Temperature, Pressure, ...

Response is Strength

Vars	R-Sq	R-Sq (adj)	R-sq (pred)	Mallows Cp	S	Temperature	Pressure	Rate	Rt to	Concentration Time
1	72.1	71.0	66.9	38.5	12.328					X
1	39.4	37.1	26.3	112.7	18.154	X				
2	85.9	84.8	81.4	9.1	8.9321			X	X	
2	82.0	80.6	74.2	17.8	10.076				X	X
3	87.4	85.9	79.0	7.6	8.5978		X	X	X	
3	86.5	84.9	81.4	9.7	8.9110	X		X	X	
4	89.1	87.3	80.6	5.8	8.1698	X	X	X	X	
4	88.0	86.0	79.3	8.2	8.5550	X		X	X	X
5	89.9	87.7	78.8	6.0	8.0390	X	X	X	X	X

We're looking for a model that has a high adjusted R-squared, a small standard error of the regression, and a Mallows' Cp close to the number of variables plus one.

The model I circled is the one that the stepwise method produced. Based on the goodness-of-fit measures, this model appears to be a good candidate. However, the best subsets regression results provide a larger context that might help us make a choice using our subject-area knowledge and goals.

Using Best Subsets Regression in conjunction with Our Requirements

We might have specific priorities that affect our choice for the best model.

For instance, if our top priorities are to simplify and reduce the costs of data collection, we might be interested in the models with fewer independent variables that fit the data nearly as well. The first model listed with three variables has an adjusted R-squared that is only 1.4 percentage points less than the circled model. In fact, the best two-variable model is not far behind.

On the other hand, if using the model to make accurate predictions is our top priority, we might be tempted to use the model with all five independent variables. Almost all of the goodness-of-fit measures are marginally better for the full model compared to the best model with four variables. However, the predicted R-squared peaks with a model that has only two variables.

Often, predicted R-squared starts to decline when the model becomes too complex and begins to fit the noise in the data. Sometimes simpler models can produce more precise predictions. For the most predictive model, we might use the best two-variable model because it has the highest predicted R-squared.

I value this extra information that best subsets regression provides. While this procedure requires more knowledge and effort to sort through the multiple models, it helps us choose the best model using our requirements. However, this method also fits many more models than stepwise regression, which increases the risk of finding chance correlations. You'll learn about the perils of fitting many models and chance correlations in the next chapter!

Assess Your Candidate Regression Models Thoroughly

If you use stepwise regression or best subsets regression to help pick your model, you need to investigate the candidate models thoroughly. That entails fitting the candidate models the normal way and checking the residual plots to be sure the fit is unbiased. You also need to assess the signs and values of the regression coefficients to be sure that they make sense. These automatic model selection procedures can find chance correlations in the sample data and produce models that don't make sense in the real world.

Automatic variable selection procedures can be helpful tools, particularly in the exploratory stage. However, you can't expect an automated algorithm to understand the subject area better than you! Be aware of the following potential problems.

- These procedures can sift through many different models and find correlations that exist by chance in the sample. Assess the results critically and use your expertise to determine whether they make sense.
- These procedures cannot take real-world knowledge into account. The model might not be correct in a practical sense.
- Stepwise regression does not always choose the model with the largest R-squared value.

We saw how stepwise and best subsets regression compare. At this point, there is a logical question. Does one of these procedures work better? Read on!

Stepwise versus Best Subsets

Which automatic variable selection procedure works better? And, how well does it work? Olejnik, Mills, and Keselman performed a simulation study to compare how frequently stepwise regression and best subsets regression choose the correct model. The results of their study are instructive both in how well the procedures work but also by identifying issues that reduce the ability to fit the correct model. The challenges that make choosing the correct model more difficult for the automated procedures will also affect your ability to fit the best model using statistical measures. Consequently, even if you don't use these automated procedures, the results of the study are worth considering. (Olejnik, Mills, & Keselman, 2000)

The authors include 32 conditions in their study that differ by the number of candidate variables, number of correct variables, sample size, and amount of multicollinearity. For each state, a computer generated 1000 datasets. The authors analyzed each dataset using both stepwise and best subsets regression. For best subsets regression, they compared the effectiveness of using the lowest Mallows' Cp to using the highest adjusted R-squared.

Drum roll, please!

The winner is ... stepwise regression!

Although, it is a very close competition. Overall, stepwise regression is better than best subsets regression using the lowest Mallows' Cp by less than 3%. Best subsets regression using the highest adjusted R-squared approach is the clear loser here.

However, there is a big warning to reveal.

Stepwise regression does not usually pick the correct model!

How Accurate is Stepwise Regression?

Let's take a closer look at the results. I'm going to cover only the step-wise results. However, best subsets regression using the lowest Mallows' Cp follows the same patterns and is virtually tied.

First, here are definitions for terms in this study.

- Authentic variables are the independent variables that truly have a relationship with the dependent variable.
- Noise variables are independent variables that do not have an actual relationship with the dependent variable.
- The correct model includes all of the authentic variables and excludes all of the noise variables.

Let's explore the accuracy of stepwise regression in picking the correct model, and the conditions that affect its accuracy.

When stepwise regression is most accurate

Let's start by looking at the best-case scenario for the stepwise procedure. In the study, this procedure is most capable when there are four candidate variables, three of the variables are authentic, there is no multicollinearity, and there is an extra-large sample size of 500 observations. This sample size is larger than the number of observations that most studies will collect when they are considering only four candidate variables.

In this scenario, stepwise regression chooses the correct model 84% of the time. The bad news is that this scenario is not realistic for most studies, and the accuracy drops from here.

The role of the number of candidate variables and authentic variables in stepwise regression accuracy

The study assesses conditions with either 4 or 8 independent variables (IVs) that are candidates. When there are more variables to evaluate, it is harder for stepwise regression to identify the correct model. This pattern also applies to the number of authentic independent variables.

The table illustrates this pattern for scenarios with no multicollinearity and a good sample size (100-120). The percentage correct decreases as the number of candidate variables and authentic variables increase. Notice how most scenarios produce the correct model less than half the time!

Candidate IVs	Authentic IVs	% Correct model
4	1	62.7
	2	54.3
	3	34.4
8	2	31.3
	4	12.7
	6	1.1

The role of multicollinearity in stepwise regression accuracy

The study also assesses the role that multicollinearity plays in the capability of stepwise regression to choose the correct model. When independent variables are correlated, it's harder to isolate the individual effect of each variable. This difficulty occurs regardless whether it is a human or computer algorithm trying to identify the correct model.

The next table illustrates how the percentage correct varies by the amount of correlation and the number of variables. The results are based on a good sample size (100-120). As the correlation increases, the percentage correct decreases.

Candidate IVs	Authentic IVs	Correlation	% Correct model
4	2	0.0	54.3
		0.2	43.1
		0.6	15.7
8	4	0.0	12.7
		0.2	1.0
		0.6	0.4

The role of sample size in stepwise regression accuracy

The study assesses two sample sizes to determine how it affects the ability of stepwise regression to choose the correct model. The smaller sample size is based on the number of observations necessary to obtain 0.80 statistical power, which is between 100-120 observations. This approach is consistent with best practices, and I've referred to this size as a "good sample size" previously.

The study also uses a very large sample size, which is five times the size of the good sample size.

The following table shows that a very large sample size improves the capability of stepwise regression to choose the correct model. Collecting a very large sample size might be more expensive, but it dramatically improves the variable selection process.

Candidate IVs	Authentic IVs	Correlation	%Correct Good sample size	%Correct Very large sample
4	2	0.0	54.3	72.1
		0.2	43.1	72.9
		0.6	15.7	69.2
8	4	0.0	12.7	53.9
		0.2	1.0	39.5
		0.6	0.4	1.8

Closing Thoughts on Choosing the Correct Model

Stepwise regression and best subsets regression don't usually pick the correct model. This finding is true with the relatively low number of candidate independent variables that the simulation study assesses. In actual studies, it would be not surprising if the researchers need to assess many more variables, which would further reduce the percentage. In fact, unlike the simulation study, you can't even be sure that you are assessing all of the authentic variables in a real-world experiment!

Given these findings, you might be asking, "are stepwise regression and best subsets regression (using the lowest Mallows' Cp) useful tools?"

I think they provide value during the very early, investigative stages of a study, particularly when theory doesn't provide much guidance. However, you must rigorously assess the candidate models to see if they make sense. Further, it is crucial to understand that stepwise regression usually only gets you closer to the correct model, but not all of the way there.

In that sense, I think stepwise regression provides some benefits. It can help you get to the right ballpark and provide a glimpse of the relationships in your data.

However, reality is complicated, and we are trying to model it with a sample. Choosing the correct model can be difficult even when researchers are armed with extensive subject-area knowledge. It is unreasonable to expect an automatic variable selection procedure to figure it out for you. Stepwise regression follows simple rules to pick the variables and it does not know anything about the study area.

It's up to you to go from the rough notion to the correct model. To do this, use your expertise, theory, and common sense rather than depending only on simple variable selection rules.

Review and Next Steps

When you're specifying a regression, there are many statistical and theoretical considerations. It is vital to do your background research in advance to help you go down the right path. After all, if you accidentally fail to measure an important variable, it can potentially invalidate your results. It's a matter of balancing theory, knowledge, and statistics. Finally, there are automated tools that can help you with this process, but they're not perfect.

CHAPTER 8

Problematic Methods of Specifying Your Model

So far, we've looked at approaches you should follow for specifying the correct model. Specifically, I shared guidelines for determining which variables to include as well as methods to help ensure that you don't accidentally exclude confounding variables. We've also looked at how you need to be on guard against adding too many variables and going beyond the natural limit of explainable variability for the outcome variable. Overall, the process requires a combination of theory and statistical measures.

Next, we'll move on to two broad model specification approaches that violate these guidelines in one way or the other. I want to show you what can go wrong when you don't apply subject-area expertise and critical thinking.

The first problematic approach is data dredging, which is when you examine many variables, combinations of variables, and different types of effects to see what sticks statistically. This approach focuses on analyzing many model terms and using statistical measures alone to choose the model at the expense of using subject-area knowledge.

The second issue is overfitting your model. This problem occurs when your model is too complicated. It begins to fit the random noise in your sample rather than relationships between variables that actually exist in the population.

Using Data Dredging and Significance

Data mining and regression seem to go together naturally. Earlier, I've described regression as a seductive analysis because it is so tempting and so easy to add more variables in the pursuit of a larger R-squared. Data mining is the opposite of the theory-based approach I discussed previously. Now, I'll illustrate the problems that data mining creates so you know why you should avoid them!

To do this, I'll show how data mining with regression analysis can take randomly generated data and produce a misleading model that appears to have significant variables and a good R-squared. Then, I'll explain how data mining creates these deceptive results and how to avoid them.

When you think of data mining, you tend to think of big data. However, it can occur on the scale of a smaller research study. In this context, it's often referred to as data dredging or a fishing expedition. However, data mining problems can be more pronounced when you're using smaller data sets. That's the context that I'm writing about.

Data dredging is the process of exploring a data set and allowing the patterns in the sample to suggest the correct model rather than being guided by theory. This process is easy because you can quickly test numerous combinations of independent variables to uncover statistically significant relationships. In fact, automated model building procedures, such as best subsets regression, can fit thousands of models quickly. You can continue adding statistically significant variables as you find them, and R-squared always increases.

Over the years, I've heard numerous comments about how it makes sense to look at many different variables, their interactions, and polynomials in all sorts of combinations. After all, if you end up with a model that is full of statistically significant variables, a high R-squared, and good-looking residual plots, what can possibly be wrong? I've literally been asked many times, "What could possibly be wrong?!" That's exactly what I'm going to show you!

Regression Example that Illustrates the Problems of Data Mining

The first thing I want to show is the severity of the problems. That way, if you use this approach, you understand the potential problems. Luckily, it's easy to demonstrate because data mining can find statistically significant correlations in data that are randomly generated. Data mining can take a set of randomly generated independent variables and use them to explain the majority of the variation in a randomly generated dependent variable. That's random data "explaining" other random data!

For this demonstration, I've created 101 columns of data, and each one contains 30 rows of entirely random data. The first column (C1) will be the dependent variable, and the other 100 columns are potential independent variables. I'll use stepwise regression to pick the model. Use this CSV data file: Random_data.

This scenario forces the procedure to dredge through 100 models just to pick the first variable, and then repeat that for the next variables. That's a lot of models to fit! We'll talk more about that later because it's a defining characteristic of data dredging.

Using Stepwise Regression on Random Data

Initially, the stepwise procedure adds 28 independent variables to the model, which explains 100% of the variance! Because we have a sample size of only 30, we're obviously overfitting the model. Overfitting a model is a different issue that also inflates R-squared. We'll get to overfitting shortly!

In this section, I want to address only the problems related to data mining, so I'll reduce the number of independent variables to avoid an overfit model. A good rule of thumb is to include a maximum of one variable for every 10 observations. With 30 observations, I'll include only the first three variables that stepwise regression picks: C35, C28, and C87. The stepwise regression output for the first three variables is below.

	----Step 1----		----Step 2----		----Step 3----	
	Coef	P	Coef	P	Coef	P
Constant	0.259		0.386		0.479	
C35	-0.520	0.001	-0.531	0.000	-0.571	0.000
C28			0.379	0.012	0.418	0.002
C87					0.373	0.005
S	0.818091		0.740015		0.644120	
R-sq	32.90%		47.06%		61.38%	
R-sq(adj)	30.51%		43.14%		56.92%	
R-sq(pred)	21.70%		33.88%		49.13%	
Mallows' Cp	19.17		11.64		4.00	

In step three, the coefficient P values are all statistically significant. The R-squared of 61.38% can be considered either strong or moderate depending on the field of study. However, for random data, it's unbelievable—literally! In actual research, you're likely to have some real effects mixed in, which can produce an even higher R-squared value.

Neither the adjusted R-squared nor the predicted R-squared indicate any problems. In fact, all three R-squared values increase with each additional term. That's what you want to see. The residual plots look good (not shown).

Just to be sure, let's graph the relationship between an independent variable (C35) and the dependent variable (C1). We'll see if it looks like a real relationship. Seeing is believing!

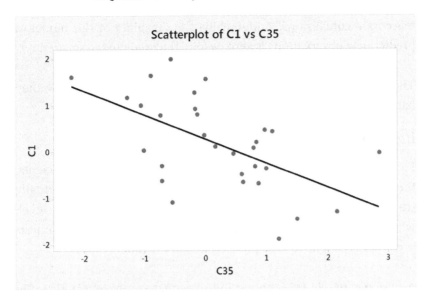

This plot looks good. The graph shows that as C35 increases, the dependent variable (C1) tends to decrease, which is consistent with the negative coefficient in the output. The data sure look like they follow a real relationship. If we didn't know that the data are random, we'd think it's a great model!

Lessons Learned from the Data Mining Example

This example shows how data mining symptoms can be hard to detect. There are no visible signs of problems even though *all* of the results are deceptive. The statistical output and chart look great. Unfortunately, these results don't reflect actual relationships but instead represent chance correlations that are guaranteed to occur with enough opportunities.

In the introduction, I asked, "What can possibly be wrong?" Now you know—everything can be wrong! The regression model suggests that random data can explain other random data, which is impossible. If you didn't already know that there are no actual relationships between these variables, these results would lead you to completely inaccurate conclusions. Additionally, the capability of this model to predict new observations is zero despite the predicted R-squared.

The problems are real. Now, let's move on to explaining how they happen and how to avoid them.

How Data Mining Causes these Problems

For all hypothesis tests, including tests for regression coefficients, there is always the chance of rejecting a null hypothesis that is actually true (Type I error). This error rate equals your significance level, which is often 5%. In other words, in cases where the null hypothesis is correct, you'll have false positives 5% of the time.

A false positive in this context indicates that you have a statistically significant P value, but no effect or relationship exists in the population. These false positives occur due to chance patterns in the sample data that are not present in the population. The more hypothesis tests you perform, the greater your probability of encountering false positives.

Let's apply these concepts to data mining with regression analysis. When you fit many models with different combinations of variables, you are performing many hypothesis tests. In fact, if you use an automated procedure like stepwise or best subsets regression, you are performing hundreds if not thousands of hypothesis tests on the same data.

With a large number of tests, you will inevitably find variables that appear to be significant but are actually false positives. If you are guided mainly by statistical significance, you'll keep these variables in the model, and it will fill up with false positives.

That's precisely what occurred in our example. We had 100 candidate independent variables and stepwise regression scoured through hundreds of potential models to find the chance correlations. As you saw, there are not necessarily any visible problems in the models you fit using data dredging techniques. It's the process of fitting many different possible models that creates the problems. Consequently, you need to be conscious of how many model combinations you fit to arrive at your final model.

Next, I'll explain how you can specify your model without using data mining and avoid these problems.

Let Theory Guide You and Avoid Data Mining

Don't get me wrong. Data mining can help build a regression model in the exploratory stage, particularly when there isn't much theory to guide you. However, if you use data mining as the primary way to specify your model, you are likely to experience some problems.

If you use data mining, perform a confirmation study using a new dataset to verify the initial results. Otherwise, you might face costly consequences. Imagine if we had made decisions based on the example model! However, if we collected another dataset, we would not have obtained the same results. Random chance that produces apparent relationships in one sample is not going to repeat itself the same way in the next sample.

Instead of data mining, use theory to guide you while fitting models and evaluating results. I know I have mentioned this several times before. But, it's true. The more you can use theory, the better your results. This approach reduces the number of models that you need to fit. Additionally, you can evaluate the model's properties using subject-area considerations.

This method requires that you review the subject-area literature and similar studies.

The advance research allows you to:

- Collect the correct data in the first place.
- Specify a good model without data mining.
- Compare your results to theory.

In conclusion, you want to develop knowledge that can guide you rather than relying on automated procedures to build your model. After all, it's unreasonable to expect simple algorithms based on statistical significance to model the complex world better than a subject-area expert. Use your smarts before brute force!

I know, I'm sounding like a broken record, but using theory when possible is that important.

Now, let's move to the problems of overfitting your model.

Overfitting Regression Models

Overfitting a model is a condition where a statistical model begins to describe the random error in the data rather than the relationships between variables. This problem occurs when the model is too complex. In regression analysis, overfitting can produce misleading R-squared values, regression coefficients, and p-values.

Overfit regression models have too many terms for the number of observations. When this occurs, the regression coefficients represent the noise rather than the genuine relationships in the population.

That's problematic by itself. However, there is another problem. Each sample has its own unique quirks. Consequently, a regression model that becomes tailor-made to fit the random quirks of one sample is unlikely to fit the random quirks of another sample. Thus, overfitting a regression model reduces its generalizability outside the original dataset.

Taking the above in combination, an overfit regression model describes the noise, and it's not applicable outside the sample. That's not very helpful, right? I'd really like these problems to sink in because overfitting often occurs when analysts chase a high R-squared. In fact, inflated R-squared values are a *symptom* of overfit models! Despite the misleading results, it can be difficult for analysts to give up that nice high R-squared value.

When choosing a regression model, our goal is to approximate the true model for the whole population. If we accomplish this goal, our model should fit most random samples drawn from that population. In other words, our results are more generalizable—we can expect that the model will fit other samples.

Graphical Illustration of Overfitting Regression Models

The image below illustrates an overfit model. The straight line represents the true relationship between the variables. The random error inherent in the data causes the data points to fall randomly around the straight fit line. The wavy line represents an overfit model. This model is too complex, and it attempts to explain the random error present in the data.

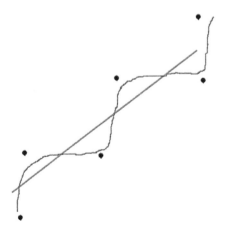

The diagram is very clear. However, it's not always that obvious. The fitted line plot shows an overfit model. In the graph, it appears that the model explains a good proportion of the dependent variable variance. Unfortunately, this is an overfit model, and I'll show you how to detect it shortly.

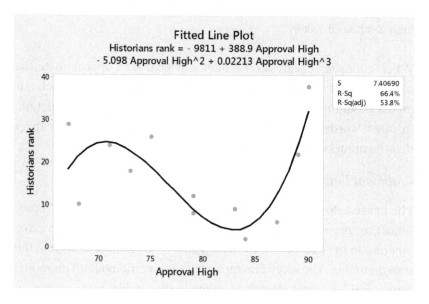

How Overfitting a Model Causes these Problems

Let's go back to the basics of inferential statistics to understand how overfitting models causes problems. You use inferential statistics to draw conclusions about a population from a random sample. Sample size is an important consideration that limits the quantity and quality of the conclusions you can draw about a population. The more you need to learn, the larger the sample must be.

This concept is fairly intuitive. Suppose we have a total sample size of 20 and we need to estimate one population mean using a 1-sample t-test. We'll probably obtain a good estimate. However, if we want to use a 2-sample t-test to estimate the means of two populations, it's not as good because we have only ten observations to estimate each mean.

If we want to estimate three or more means using one-way ANOVA, it becomes pretty bad.

As the number of observations per estimate decreases (20, 10, 6.7, etc.), the estimates become more erratic. Furthermore, a new sample is unlikely to replicate the inconsistent estimates produced by the smaller sample sizes.

In short, the quality of the estimates deteriorates as you draw more conclusions from a sample. This idea is directly related to the degrees of freedom in the analysis.

Applying These Concepts to Overfitting Regression Models

Overfitting a regression model is similar to the previous example. The problems occur when you try to estimate too many parameters from the sample. Each term in the model forces the regression analysis to estimate a parameter using a fixed sample size. Therefore, the size of your sample restricts the number of terms that you can safely add to the model before you obtain erratic estimates.

Similar to the example with the means, you need a sufficient number of observations for each term in the regression model to help ensure trustworthy results. Statisticians have conducted simulation studies which indicate you should have at least 10-15 observations for each term in a linear model. The number of terms in a model is the sum of all the independent variables, their interactions, and polynomial terms to model curvature. (Babyak, 2004)

For instance, if the regression model has two independent variables and their interaction term, you have three terms and need 30-45 observations. Although, if the model has multicollinearity or if the effect size is small, you might require more observations.

To obtain reliable results, you need a sample size that is large enough to handle the model complexity that your study requires. If your study calls for a complex model, you must collect a relatively large sample size. If the sample is too small, you can't dependably fit a model that approaches the true model for your independent variable. In that case, the results can be misleading.

How to Detect Overfit Models

As I discussed earlier, generalizability suffers in an overfit model. Consequently, you can detect overfitting by determining whether your model fits new data as well as it fits the data used to estimate the model. In statistics, we call this cross-validation, and it often involves partitioning your data.

However, for linear regression, there is an excellent accelerated cross-validation method called predicted R-squared, which I covered back in chapter 6. This method doesn't require you to collect a separate sample or partition your data, and you can obtain the cross-validated results as you fit the model. Statistical software calculates predicted R-squared using the following automated procedure:

- It removes a data point from the dataset.
- Calculates the regression equation.
- Evaluates how well the model predicts the missing observation.
- And, repeats this for all data points in the dataset.

Predicted R-squared has several cool features. First, you can just include it in the output as you fit the model without any extra steps on your part. Second, it's easy to interpret. You simply compare predicted R-squared to the regular R-squared and see if there is a big difference.

If there is a large discrepancy between the two values, your model doesn't predict new observations as well as it fits the original dataset. The results are not generalizable, and there's a good chance you're overfitting the model.

For the previous fitted line plot, the model produces a predicted R-squared (as shown in chapter 6) of 0%, which reveals the overfitting.

How to Avoid Overfitting Models

To avoid overfitting a regression model, you should draw a random sample that is large enough to handle all of the terms that you expect to include in your model. This process requires that you investigate similar studies before you collect data. The goal is to identify relevant variables and terms that you are likely to include in your own model. After you get a sense of the typical complexity of models in your study area, you'll be able to estimate a good sample size.

Again, this advance planning is yet another example of how subject-area research helps you out!

Review and Next Steps

Over the past two chapters, I've shown you some suitable methods for specifying the model, and others that you should avoid! The problematic processes in this chapter were the following:

- **Data dredging**: Trying many different models and seeing what sticks by focusing on statistical significance.
- **Overfitting**: Fitting a model that is too complex given the sample size by including too many independent variables, polynomials, and interaction terms.

Both of these problems can produce misleading coefficients and inflated R-squared values.

Planning can help you avoid these problems by identifying the variables you will likely need to include in the model. This process helps you plan your data collection plan, sample size requirement, and model fitting process. Never underestimate the value of using your subject-area knowledge during this process. Your expertise helps you fit the correct model without data dredging and aids in the detection of coefficients that don't match theory, which can be a sign of various problems. Statistical measures can help you decide which variables to include, but they shouldn't be the sole deciding factor.

Next, we're going to tackle the assumptions behind regression analysis. The basis behind these assumptions frequently relates to the characteristics of the residuals. The overarching goal of the next chapter is that if your model violates any of these assumptions, you might not be able to trust any of the statistical measures that we've covered thus far! But, don't worry, I'll show you how to detect and, if necessary, correct problems.

CHAPTER 9

Checking Assumptions and Fixing Problems

Regression is a potent analysis that can analyze multiple variables simultaneously to answer complex research questions. However, like other statistical procedures, regression analysis has assumptions that you need to meet, or the results can be unreliable. In this chapter, you'll learn about the assumptions for ordinary least squares regression, how to check them, and how to correct problems. This knowledge will give you confidence in the results that you obtain.

As I've indicated earlier, I've struggled to decide where to place this chapter. You can't trust any of the statistical measures that we have covered until you specify a model that satisfies the assumptions. However, this chapter didn't seem to fit earlier because it assumes that you already know the previous information.

Always keep in mind that regression is an iterative process. Specify a model, take a peek at the statistical output, but then quickly check the residual plots before you get too invested in interpreting the results for a model that might have an obvious assumption violation.

Ordinary Least Squares (OLS) is the most common estimation method for linear models—and that's true for a good reason. The Gauss-Markov theorem states that OLS produces estimates that are better than estimates from all other linear model estimation methods when the assumptions hold true. In technical terms, when your OLS regression model satisfies the assumptions, the procedure generates unbiased coefficient estimates that tend to be relatively close to the true population values (minimum variance).

While proving the theorem goes beyond the scope of this book, it's nice knowing that OLS can provide the best estimates! Statisticians *have* proven it mathematically.

Let's dive into residuals, the theory behind them, and some examples. We covered the residuals and how OLS minimizes the sum of the squared residuals (SSE) in chapter 2. Now, we'll explore them in more depth. In regression, you verify the assumptions primarily by assessing the residual plots. Then, we'll go over the assumptions themselves and how to identify and correct potential problems.

Check Your Residual Plots!

After reading about the necessity of checking your residual plots throughout this book, you're finally going to learn all about them!

Residual plots display the residual values on the y-axis and fitted values, time-order, or another variable, on the x-axis. After you fit a regression model, it is crucial to check the residual plots. If your plots display patterns rather randomness, you can't trust the regression coefficients and other numeric results. In this section, I explain the conceptual reasons why residual plots help ensure that your regression model is valid. I'll also show you what to look for and how to fix the problems.

First, let's go over a couple of basics.

There are two fundamental parts to regression models, the deterministic and random components. If your model is not random where it supposed to be random, it has problems, and this is where residual plots come in.

The essential parts of a regression model:

Dependent Variable = (Constant +Independent Variables) + Error

Or:

Dependent Variable = Deterministic + Stochastic

Deterministic Component

The deterministic component is the portion of the variation in the dependent variable that the independent variables explain. In other words, the mean of the dependent variable is a function of the independent variables. In a regression model, all of the explanatory power should reside here.

Stochastic Error

Stochastic just means unpredictable. In statistics, the error is the difference between the expected value and the observed value. Let's put these terms together—the gap between the expected and observed values must not be predictable. Or, no explanatory power should be in the error. If you can use the error to make predictions about the response, your model has a problem. This issue is where residual plots play a role.

The theory here is that the deterministic component of a regression model does such a great job of explaining the dependent variable that it leaves only the intrinsically inexplicable portion of your study area for the error. If you can identify non-randomness in the error term, your independent variables are not explaining everything that they can.

Many of the ordinary least squares assumptions describe properties of the error term. Unfortunately, the error term is a population value that we'll never know. Instead, we'll use the next best thing that is available—the residuals. Residuals are the sample estimate of the error for each observation. The residuals estimate the true error in the same manner that regression coefficients estimate the true population co-efficients. When it comes to checking OLS assumptions, assessing the residuals is crucial!

Don't worry. This is actually easy to understand. It just means that you should not be able to see patterns in the residual plots!

How to Check Residual Plots

When looking at residual plots, you simply want to determine whether the residuals are consistent with random error. I'll use an analogy of rolling a die. You shouldn't be able to use one roll to predict the outcome of the next roll because it is supposed to be random. So, if you record a series of tosses, you should see only random results. If you start to see patterns, you know something is wrong with your model of how the die works. You think it's random, but it's not. If you were a gambler, you'd use this information to adjust how you play to match the actual die outcomes better.

You can apply this idea to regression models too. If you look at a series of errors, it should look random. If there are patterns in the errors, you can use one error to predict another. As with the die analogy, if there are patterns in the residuals, you need to adjust your model. But, don't fret, this just means you can improve the fit of the model by moving this predictability over to the deterministic side of things (i.e., your independent variables).

How do you determine whether the residuals are random in regression analysis? It's pretty simple, just check that they are randomly scattered around zero for the entire range of fitted values. Being centered on zero indicates that the model's predictions tend to be on target rather than systematically too high or low. The hypothesis tests in regression assume that the residuals follow a normal distribution and that the degree of scattering is the same for all fitted values.

Residuals should look like this.

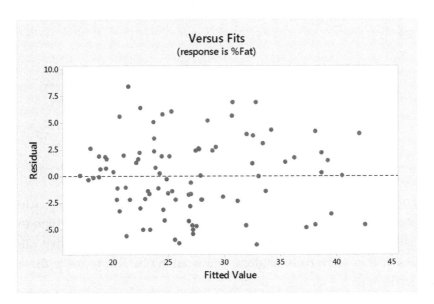

How to Fix Problematic Residual Plots

The following residual plot clearly has a pattern! In this case, it indicates that the model is not fitting curvature that is present in the data.

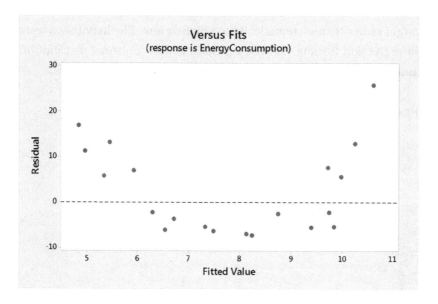

For the above model, if you know the fitted value, you can use it to predict the residual. For instance, fitted values near 5 and 10 tend to have positive residuals. Fitted values near 7 tend to have negative values. If they were truly random, you wouldn't be able to make these predictions.

This residual plot indicates that the independent variables do not capture the entire deterministic component. Some of the explanatory information has leaked over to the supposedly random error. There are a variety of reasons why a model can have this problem. The possibilities include a missing:

- Independent variable.
- Polynomial term to model a curve (See plot above).
- Interaction term.
- Time-order effect.

To fix the problem, you need to identify the missing information, variable, or higher-order term and include it in the model. There is no one-size fits all solution. You'll need to assess the residual plots, apply subject-area knowledge, and try modifying the model. Identifying the resolution requires subject-area knowledge and research. The solution is very particular to your research. After you correct the problem and refit the model, the residuals should look nice and random!

Residual Plots are Easy!

Hopefully, you see that checking your residuals plots is a crucial but simple thing to do. You need random residuals. Your independent variables should describe the relationship so thoroughly that only random error remains. Non-random patterns in your residuals signify that your variables are missing something.

Importantly, appreciate that if you do see unwanted patterns in your residual plots, it actually represents a chance to improve your model because there is something more that it can explain. Furthermore, the pattern can help you identify the problem and solution. That's all good!

Now we'll systematically go into more depth about the assumptions themselves and how to check them using residual plots (mainly).

The Seven Classical OLS Assumptions

When the seven classical OLS assumptions hold true, the procedure produces the best estimates. However, when your model does not satisfy some of these assumptions, you might need to employ remedial measures or use other estimation methods to improve the results.

The first six assumptions are mandatory to produce the best estimates. Even though the quality of the estimates does not depend on the seventh assumption, analysts often evaluate it for other important reasons that I'll cover.

OLS Assumption 1: The correctly specified regression model is linear in the coefficients and the error term

This assumption addresses the following two properties of the model:

- The linear functional form of the model.
- The accuracy in which it describes the real relationships of the subject matter.

In statistics, a regression model is linear when all terms in the model are either the constant or a parameter multiplied by an independent variable. You build the model equation only by adding the terms together. These rules constrain the model to one type:

$$y = \beta_0 + \beta_1 X_1 + \beta_2 X_2 + \cdots + \beta_k X_k + \varepsilon$$

In the equation, the betas (βs) are the parameters that OLS estimates. Epsilon (ε) is the random error.

As I explained earlier, the defining characteristic of linear regression is this functional form of the *parameters* rather than the ability to model curvature. Linear models can model curvature by including nonlinear *variables* such as polynomials and transforming exponential functions.

To satisfy this assumption, the correctly specified model must fit the linear pattern. We covered this assumption in the curve fitting in Chapter 4. If you can't adequately model the curvature using a linear model, you will likely need to use a different type of regression, such as nonlinear regression or a generalized linear model.

In addition to following the linear function form, your model should accurately describe the real relationships among variables. It should include all relevant independent variables, fit curvature that is present, and include the appropriate interaction effects. In short, your model needs to portray the subject matter accurately. If the model is not an accurate representation, statisticians call it a model specification error.

For example, a specification error occurs when you omit an essential variable, fail to fit the curvature, or exclude appropriate interaction terms among other possibilities. In other words, when your model doesn't accurately depict reality using a linear model, it violates the first OLS assumption.

Specification errors often cause failures in some of the other assumptions. For example, in chapter 7, we saw how omitting a confounding variable violates assumption #3, which can bias the coefficient estimates. Additionally, normally distributed residuals (#7) can be difficult to obtain if you exclude an important variable or incorrectly fit curvature.

As we go through the remaining six assumptions, keep in mind that violations of those assumptions might actually represent a specification error. The first and simplest solutions I'd try are adding variables, using a different technique to model the curvature, and adding interaction terms.

If you exhaust the more straightforward approaches, you might need to try more complex solutions. These other solutions include data transformations and using a different type of regression analysis altogether. Later in this chapter, you'll learn about data transformations, and I cover alternative regression methods at the end of the book—although you learned a little about nonlinear regression in chapter 4.

OLS Assumption 2: The error term has a population mean of zero

The error term accounts for the variation in the dependent variable that the independent variables do not explain. Random chance should determine the values of the error term. For your model to be unbiased, the average value of the error term must equal zero.

After all, if the average error is +7, this non-zero error indicates that our model systematically underpredicts the observed values. Statisticians refer to systematic error like this as bias, and it signifies that our model is inadequate because it is not correct on average.

Stated another way, we want the expected value of the error to equal zero. If the expected value is +7 rather than zero, part of the error term is predictable, and we should add that information to the regression model itself. We want only random error left for the error term.

You don't need to worry about this assumption when you include the constant in your regression model because it forces the mean of the residuals to equal zero. For more information about this assumption, read the section about the regression constant in Chapter 3.

OLS Assumption 3: All independent variables are uncorrelated with the error term

If an independent variable is correlated with the error term, we can use the independent variable to predict the error term, which violates the notion that the error term represents unpredictable random error. We need to find a way to incorporate that information into the regression model itself.

This assumption is also referred to as exogeneity. Conversely, when this type of correlation exists, which violates the assumption, there is endogeneity. Violations of this assumption can occur because there is simultaneity between the independent and dependent variables, omitted variable bias, incorrectly modeled curvature, or measurement error in the independent variables.

Violating this assumption biases the coefficient estimate. To understand why this bias occurs, keep in mind that the error term always explains some of the variability in the dependent variable. However, when an independent variable is correlated with the error term, OLS incorrectly attributes some of the variance that the error term actually explains to the independent variable instead.

To check this assumption, graph the residuals by each independent variable. The graph should display that nice randomness I showed earlier. If there is a pattern, your model has a problem. You'll need to investigate to determine the cause. At least you'll know which variable is associated with the violation!

The residual plot displays an example where Energy Consumption (the independent variable) correlates with the residuals because the model doesn't adequately fit curvature in the data. For this example, we need to include a squared term Energy Consumption to fix the problem.

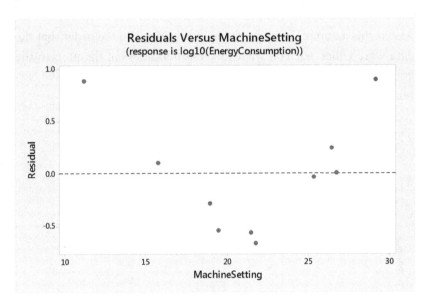

In Chapter 7, I explained how confounding variables are problematic because they violate this assumption. Read that chapter for more ideas about how to address this problem.

OLS Assumption 4: Observations of the error term are uncorrelated with each other

One observation of the error term should not predict the next observation. For instance, if the error for one observation is positive and that systematically increases the probability that the following error is positive, that is a positive correlation. If the subsequent error is more likely to have the opposite sign, that is a negative correlation. This problem is known both as serial correlation and autocorrelation. Serial correlation is most likely to occur in time series models.

For example, if sales are unexpectedly high on one day, then they are likely to be higher than average on the next day. This isn't an unreasonable expectation for some subject areas, such as inflation rates, GDP, unemployment, and so on.

Assess this assumption by graphing the residuals in the order that the data were collected. You want to see randomness in the plot. In the graph for a sales model, there is a cyclical pattern with a positive correlation.

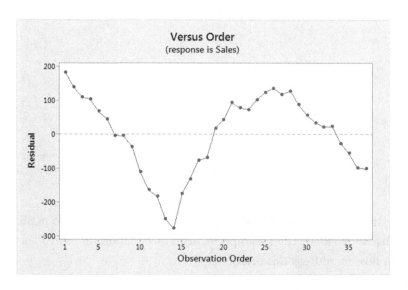

As I've explained, if you have information that allows you to predict the error term for an observation, you must incorporate that information into the model itself. To resolve this issue, you might need to add an independent variable to the model that captures this information. Analysts commonly use distributed lag models, which use both current values of the dependent variable and past values of independent variables.

For the sales model, we need to add variables that explains the cyclical pattern.

Using regression analysis to analyze time ordered data is possible, but it has a number of unique challenges, which go beyond the scope of this introductory book. You can also try fitting a time series model rather than a regression model.

Serial correlation reduces the precision of OLS estimates.

OLS Assumption 5: The error term has a constant variance (no heteroscedasticity)

The variance of the errors should be consistent for all observations. In other words, the variance does not change for each observation or for a range of observations. This preferred condition is known as homoscedasticity (same scatter). If the variance changes, we refer to that as heteroscedasticity (different scatter).

The easiest way to check this assumption is to create a residuals versus fitted values plot. On this type of graph, heteroscedasticity appears as a cone shape where the spread of the residuals increases in one direction. In the following graph, the spread of the residuals increases as the fitted values increase.

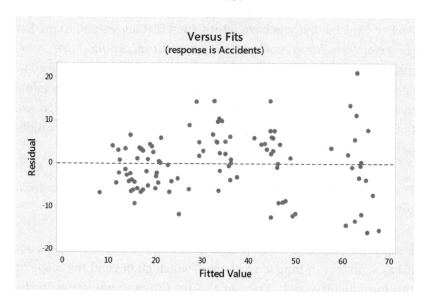

Versus Fits
(response is Accidents)

Heteroscedasticity reduces the precision of the estimates in OLS linear regression. I'll cover heteroscedasticity and potential solutions in more detail in the next section.

Note: When assumption 4 (no autocorrelation) and 5 (homoscedasticity) are both true, statisticians say that the error term is independent and identically distributed (IID) and refer to them as spherical errors.

OLS Assumption 6: No independent variable is a perfect linear function of other explanatory variables

Perfect correlation occurs when two variables have a Pearson's correlation coefficient of +1 or -1. When one of the variables changes, the other variable also changes by a completely fixed proportion. The two variables move in unison.

Perfect correlation suggests that two variables are different forms of the same variable. For example, games won and games lost have a perfect negative correlation (-1). The temperature in Fahrenheit and Celsius have a perfect positive correlation (+1).

Ordinary least squares cannot distinguish one variable from the other when they are perfectly correlated. If you specify a model that contains independent variables with perfect correlation, your statistical software can't fit the model, and it will display an error message. You must remove one of the variables from the model to proceed.

Perfect correlation is a show stopper. However, your statistical software can fit OLS regression models with imperfect but strong relationships between the independent variables. If these correlations are high enough, they can cause problems. Statisticians refer to this condition as multicollinearity, and it reduces the precision of the estimates in OLS linear regression.

You'll learn more about multicollinearity later in this chapter.

OLS Assumption 7: The error term is normally distributed (optional)

OLS does not require that the error term follows a normal distribution to produce unbiased estimates with the minimum variance. However, satisfying this assumption allows you to perform statistical hypothesis testing and generate reliable confidence intervals and prediction intervals.

The easiest way to determine whether the residuals follow a normal distribution is to assess a normal probability plot. If the residuals follow the straight line on this type of graph, they are normally distributed. They look good on the plot!

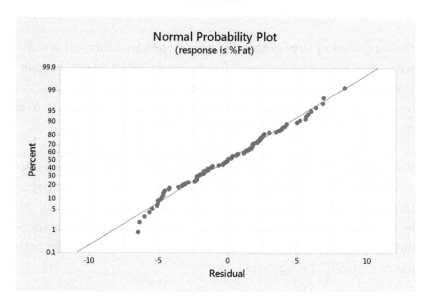

If you need to obtain p-values for the coefficient estimates and the overall test of significance, check this assumption!

I'm often asked whether OLS assumes that the variables themselves are normally distributed. No, it does not. This assumption refers to the residuals and not the distribution of the variables. In fact, the body fat dependent variable I use for the BMI model in Chapter 10 is moderately skewed, yet the residuals follow a normal distribution. These residuals are shown in the normal probability plot. However, if the dependent variable is very non-normal, it might be more difficult for the residuals to satisfy this assumption. In this case, using a data transformation can help.

Why You Should Care About the Classical OLS Assumptions

In a nutshell, your linear model should produce residuals that have a mean of zero, have a constant variance, and are not correlated with themselves or other variables. The residual plots should not display any patterns.

If these assumptions hold true, the OLS procedure creates the best possible estimates. In statistics, estimators that produce unbiased estimates that have the smallest variance are referred to as being "efficient." Efficiency is a statistical concept that compares the quality of the estimates calculated by different procedures while holding the sample size constant. OLS is the most efficient linear regression estimator when the assumptions hold true.

Another benefit of satisfying these assumptions is that as the sample size increases to infinity, the coefficient estimates converge on the actual population parameters.

If your error term also follows the normal distribution, you can safely use hypothesis testing to determine whether the independent variables and the entire model are statistically significant. You can also produce reliable confidence intervals and prediction intervals.

Knowing that you're maximizing the value of your data by using the most efficient methodology to obtain the best possible estimates should set your mind at ease. It's worthwhile checking these OLS assumptions! The best way to assess them is by using residual plots.

Next Steps

Now, we'll look into heteroscedasticity and multicollinearity in more detail and explore solutions.

Heteroscedasticity

Heteroscedasticity means unequal scatter. In regression analysis, we talk about heteroscedasticity in the context of the residuals or error term. Specifically, heteroscedasticity is a systematic change in the spread of the residuals over the range of measured values. Heteroscedasticity is a problem because ordinary least squares (OLS) regression assumes that all residuals are drawn from a population that has a constant variance (homoscedasticity).

To satisfy the regression assumptions and be able to trust the results, the residuals should have a constant variance. In this section, I show you how to identify heteroscedasticity, explain what produces it, the problems it causes, and work through an example to show you several solutions.

How to Identify Heteroscedasticity with Residual Plots

Let's start with how you detect heteroscedasticity because that is easy.

Heteroscedasticity produces a distinctive fan or cone shape in residual plots. To check for heteroscedasticity, you need to assess the residuals by fitted value plots specifically. Typically, the telltale pattern for heteroscedasticity is that as the fitted values increases, the variance of the residuals also increases.

You can see an example of this cone shaped pattern in the residuals by fitted value plot. Note how the vertical range of the residuals increases as the fitted values increases. Later in this section, we'll return to the model that produces this plot when we try to fix the problem and produce homoscedasticity.

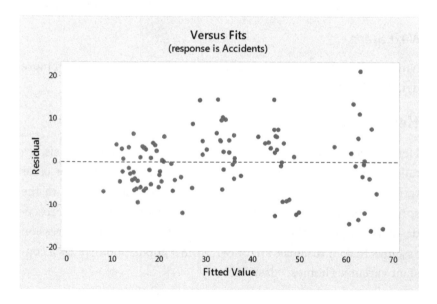

What Causes Heteroscedasticity?

Heteroscedasticity, also spelled heteroskedasticity, occurs more often in datasets that have a large range between the largest and smallest observed values. While there are numerous reasons why heteroscedasticity can exist, a common explanation is that the error variance changes proportionally with a factor. This factor might be a variable in the model.

In some cases, the variance increases proportionally with this factor but remains constant as a percentage. For instance, a 10% change in a number such as 100 is much smaller than a 10% change in a large number such as 100,000. In this scenario, you expect to see larger residuals associated with higher values. That's why you need to be careful when working with wide ranges of values!

Because large ranges are associated with this problem, some types of models are more prone to heteroscedasticity.

Heteroscedasticity in cross-sectional studies

Cross-sectional studies often have very small and large values and, thus, are more likely to have heteroscedasticity. For example, a cross-sectional study that involves the United States can have very low values for Delaware and very high values for California. Similarly, cross-sectional studies of incomes can have a range that extends from poverty to billionaires.

Heteroscedasticity in time-series models

A time-series model can have heteroscedasticity if the dependent variable changes significantly from the beginning to the end of the series. For example, if we model the sales of DVD players from their first sales in 2000 to the present, the number of units sold will be vastly different. Additionally, if you're modeling time series data and measurement error changes over time, heteroscedasticity can be present because regression analysis includes measurement error in the error term. For example, if measurement error decreases over time as better methods are introduced, you'd expect the error variance to diminish over time as well.

Example of heteroscedasticity

Let's take a look at a classic example of heteroscedasticity. If you model household consumption based on income, you'll find that the variability in consumption increases as income increases. Lower income households are less variable in absolute terms because they need to focus on necessities and there is less room for different spending habits. Higher income households can purchase a wide variety of luxury items, or not, which results in a broader spread of spending habits.

Pure versus impure heteroscedasticity

Statisticians categorize heteroscedasticity into two general types.

- Pure heteroscedasticity refers to cases where you specify the correct model and yet you observe non-constant variance in the residual plots.
- Impure heteroscedasticity refers to cases where you incorrectly specify the model, and that causes the non-constant variance. When you leave an important variable out of a model, the omitted effect is absorbed into the error term. If the effect of the omitted variable varies throughout the observed range of data, it can produce the telltale signs of heteroscedasticity in the residual plots.

When you observe heteroscedasticity in the residual plots, it is important to determine whether you have pure or impure heteroscedasticity because the solutions are different. If you have the impure form, you need to identify the important variable(s) that have been left out of the model and refit the model with those variables. For the remainder of this section, I talk about the pure form of heteroscedasticity.

The causes for heteroscedasticity vary widely by subject-area. If you detect heteroscedasticity in your model, you'll need to use your expertise to understand why it occurs. Often, the key is to identify the proportional factor that is associated with the changing variance.

What Problems Does Heteroscedasticity Cause?

As I mentioned earlier, linear regression assumes that the spread of the residuals is constant across the plot. Anytime that you violate an assumption, there is a chance that you can't trust the statistical results.

Why fix this problem? There are two big reasons why you want homoscedasticity:

- While heteroscedasticity does not cause bias in the coefficient estimates, it does make them less precise. Lower precision increases the likelihood that the coefficient estimates are further from the correct population value.
- Heteroscedasticity tends to produce p-values that are smaller than they should be. This effect occurs because heteroscedasticity increases the variance of the coefficient estimates but the OLS procedure does not detect this increase. Consequently, OLS calculates the t-values and F-values using an underestimated amount of variance. This problem can lead you to conclude that a model term is statistically significant when it is actually not significant.

If you see the characteristic fan shape in your residual plots, what should you do? Read on!

How to Fix Heteroscedasticity

If you can figure out the reason for the heteroscedasticity, you might be able to correct it and improve your model. I'll show you three common approaches for turning heteroscedasticity into homoscedasticity.

To illustrate these solutions, we'll use an example cross-sectional study to model the number of automobile accidents by the population of towns and cities. These data are fictional, but they correctly illustrate the problem and how to resolve it. Use this CSV data file to try it yourself: Heteroscedasticity. We'll use Accident as the dependent variable and Population for the independent variable.

Imagine that we just fit the model and produced the residuals by fitted values plot that I showed earlier in this section. The fan shape in that plot indicates we have heteroscedasticity.

Cross-sectional studies have a larger risk of residuals with non-constant variance because of the larger disparity between the largest and smallest values. For our study, imagine the huge range of populations from towns to the major cities!

Generally speaking, you should identify the source of the non-constant variance to resolve the problem. A good place to start is a variable that has a large range.

We've detected heteroscedasticity, now what can we do about it? There are various methods for resolving this issue. I'll cover three methods that I list in my order of preference. My preference is based on minimizing the amount of data manipulation. You might need to try several approaches to see which one works best. These methods are appropriate for pure heteroscedasticity but are not necessarily valid for the impure form.

Redefining the variables

If your model is a cross-sectional model that includes large differences between the sizes of the observations, you can find different ways to specify the model that reduces the impact of the size differential. To do this, change the model from using the raw measure to using rates and per capita values. Of course, this type of model answers a slightly different kind of question. You'll need to determine whether this approach is suitable for both your data and what you need to learn.

I prefer this method when it is appropriate because it involves the least amount of tinkering with the original data. You adjust only the specific variables that need to be changed in a manner that often makes sense. Indeed, this practice forces you to think about different ways to specify your model, which frequently improves it beyond just removing heteroscedasticity.

For our original model, we were using population to predict the number of accidents. If you think about it, it isn't surprising that larger cities have more accidents. That's not particularly enlightening.

However, we can change the model so that we use population to predict the accident *rate*. This approach discounts the impact of scale and gets to the underlying behavior. Let's try this with our example data set. I'll use Accident Rate as the dependent variable and Population as the independent variable.

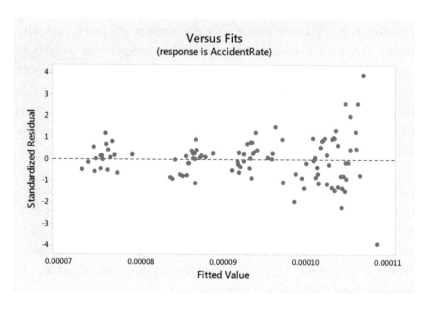

The residuals by fitted value plot looks better. If it weren't for a few pesky values in the very high range, it would be useable. If this approach had produced homoscedasticity, I would stick with this solution and not use the following methods.

Weighted least squares regression

Weighted least squares regression is a method that assigns each data point a weight based on the variance of its fitted value. The idea is to give small weights to observations associated with higher variances to shrink their squared residuals. Weighted regression minimizes the sum of the weighted squared residuals. When you use the correct weights, heteroscedasticity is replaced by homoscedasticity.

I prefer this approach somewhat less than redefining the variables. For one thing, weighted regression involves more data manipulation because it applies the weights to all variables. It's also less intuitive. And, if you skip straight to this, you might miss the opportunity to specify a more meaningful model by redefining the variables.

For our data, we know that higher populations are associated with higher variances. Consequently, we need to assign lower weights to observations of large populations. Finding the theoretically correct weight can be difficult. However, when you can identify a variable that is associated with the changing variance, a common approach is to use the inverse of that variable as the weight. In our case, the Weight column in the dataset equals 1 / Population.

I'll go back to using Accidents as the dependent variable and Population as the independent variable. However, I'll tell the software to perform weighted regression and apply the column of weights. For weighted regression, it is important to assess the standardized residuals because only that type of residual will show us that weighted regression fixed the heteroscedasticity.

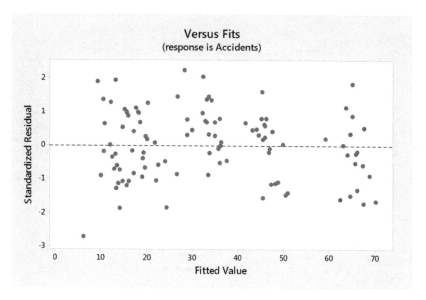

This residual plot looks great! The variance of the residuals is constant across the full range of fitted values. Homoscedasticity!

Transform the dependent variable

I always save transforming the data for the last resort because it involves the most manipulation. It also makes interpreting the results very difficult because the original units of your data are gone. The idea is that you transform your original data into different values that produce good looking residuals. If nothing else works, try a transformation to produce homoscedasticity. You'll learn more about transformations later in this chapter. For now, consider this a sneak preview!

I'll refit the original model but use a Box-Cox transformation on the dependent variable.

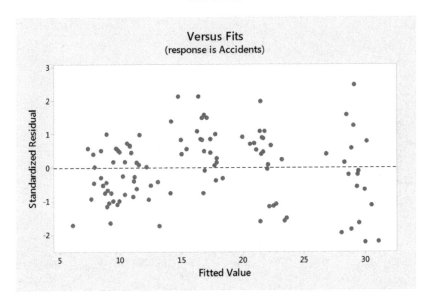

As you can see, the data transformation didn't produce homoscedasticity in this dataset. That's good because I didn't want to use this approach anyway! We'll stick with the weighted regression model.

Keep in mind that there are many different reasons for heteroscedasticity. Identifying the cause and resolving the problem in order to produce homoscedasticity can require extensive subject-area knowledge. In most cases, remedial actions for severe heteroscedasticity are necessary. However, if your primary goal is to predict the total amount of the dependent variable rather than estimating the specific effects of the independent variables, you might not need to correct non-constant variance.

Multicollinearity

Multicollinearity occurs when independent variables in a regression model are correlated. This correlation is a problem because independent variables should be independent. If the degree of correlation between variables is high enough, it can cause problems when you fit the model and interpret the results.

In this section, I highlight the problems that multicollinearity can cause, show you how to test your model for it, and highlight some ways to resolve it. In some cases, multicollinearity isn't necessarily a problem, and I'll show you how to make that determination. I'll work through an example dataset which contains multicollinearity to bring it all to life!

Why is Multicollinearity a Potential Problem?

A key goal of regression analysis is to isolate the relationship between each independent variable and the dependent variable. The interpretation of a regression coefficient is that it represents the mean change in the dependent variable for each one-unit change in an independent variable when you *hold all of the other independent variables constant*. That last portion is crucial for our discussion about multicollinearity.

The idea is that you can change the value of one independent variable and not the others. However, when independent variables are correlated, it indicates that changes in one variable are associated with shifts in another variable. The stronger the correlation, the more difficult it is to change one variable without changing another. It becomes difficult for the model to estimate the relationship between each independent variable and the dependent variable *independently* because the independent variables tend to change in unison.

There are two basic kinds of multicollinearity:

- **Structural multicollinearity**: This type occurs when we create a model term using other terms. In other words, it's a by-product of the model that we specify rather than being present in the data itself. For example, if you square term X to model curvature, clearly there is a correlation between X and X^2.
- **Data multicollinearity**: This type of multicollinearity is present in the data itself rather than being an artifact of our

model. Observational experiments are more likely to exhibit this kind of multicollinearity.

What Problems Do Multicollinearity Cause?

Multicollinearity causes the following two basic types of problems:

- The coefficient estimates can swing wildly based on which other independent variables are in the model. The coefficients become very sensitive to small changes in the model.
- Multicollinearity reduces the precision of the estimate coefficients, which weakens the statistical power of your regression model. You might not be able to trust the p-values to identify independent variables that are statistically significant.

Imagine you fit a regression model and the coefficient values, and even the signs, change dramatically depending on the specific variables that you include in the model. It's a disconcerting feeling when slightly different models lead to very different conclusions. You don't feel like you know the actual effect of each variable!

Now, throw in the fact that you can't necessarily trust the p-values to select the independent variables to include in the model. This problem makes it difficult both to specify the correct model and to justify the model if many of your p-values are not statistically significant.

As the severity of the multicollinearity increases so do these problematic effects. However, these issues affect only those independent variables that are correlated. You can have a model with severe multicollinearity and yet some variables in the model can be completely unaffected.

The regression example with multicollinearity that I work through later on illustrates these problems in action.

Do I Have to Fix Multicollinearity?

Multicollinearity makes it hard to interpret your coefficients, and it reduces the power of your model to identify independent variables that are statistically significant. These are definitely serious problems. However, the good news is that you don't always have to find a way to fix multicollinearity.

The need to reduce multicollinearity depends on its severity and your primary goal for your regression model. Keep the following three points in mind:

1. The severity of the problems increases with the degree of the multicollinearity. Therefore, if you have only moderate multicollinearity, you may not need to resolve it.
2. Multicollinearity affects only the specific independent variables that are correlated. Therefore, if multicollinearity is not present for the independent variables that you are particularly interested in, you might not need to resolve it. Suppose your model contains the experimental variables of interest and some control variables. If high multicollinearity exists for the control variables but not the experimental variables, then you can interpret the experimental variables without problems.
3. Multicollinearity affects the coefficients and p-values, but it does not influence the predictions, precision of the predictions, and the goodness-of-fit statistics. If your primary goal is to make predictions, and you don't need to understand the role of each independent variable, you don't need to reduce severe multicollinearity.

Over the years, I've found that many people are incredulous over the third point, so here's a reference! (Neter, Kutner, Nachtsheim, & Wasserman, 1996)

> *The fact that some or all predictor variables are correlated among themselves does not, in general, inhibit our ability to obtain a good fit nor does it tend to affect inferences about mean responses or predictions of new observations. —Applied Linear Statistical Models, p289, 4th Edition.*

You can use the fact that multicollinearity affects p-values but not R-squared to detect its presence. If adding a particular variable to the model causes R-squared to increase notably, but that variable is not statistically significant, you might be seeing the significance masking effects of multicollinearity. However, VIFs are a more direct way to detect multicollinearity.

Testing for Multicollinearity with Variance Inflation Factors (VIFs)

If you can identify which variables are affected by multicollinearity and the strength of the correlation, you're well on your way to determining whether you need to fix it. Fortunately, there is a very simple test to assess multicollinearity in your regression model. The variance inflation factor (VIF) identifies correlation between independent variables and the strength of that correlation.

Statistical software calculates a VIF for each independent variable. VIFs start at 1 and have no upper limit. A value of 1 indicates that there is no correlation between this independent variable and any others. VIFs between 1 and 5 suggest that there is a moderate correlation, but it is not severe enough to warrant corrective measures. VIFs greater than 5 represent critical levels of multicollinearity where the coefficients are poorly estimated, and the p-values are questionable.

Use VIFs to identify correlations between variables and determine the strength of the relationships. Most statistical software can display VIFs for you. Assessing VIFs is particularly important for observational studies because these studies are more prone to having multicollinearity.

Multicollinearity Example: Predicting Bone Density in the Femur

This regression example uses a subset of variables that I collected for an experiment. In this example, I'll show you how to detect multicollinearity as well as illustrate its effects. I'll also show you how to remove structural multicollinearity. Use this CSV data file for the example: MulticollinearityExample.

I'll use regression analysis to model the relationship between the independent variables (physical activity, body fat percentage, weight, and the interaction between weight and body fat) and the dependent variable (bone mineral density of the femoral neck).

Here are the regression results:

Regression Analysis: Femoral Neck versus %Fat, Weight kg, Activity

Analysis of Variance

Source	DF	Adj SS	Adj MS	F-Value	P-Value
Regression	4	0.555785	0.138946	27.95	0.000
%Fat	1	0.009240	0.009240	1.86	0.176
Weight kg	1	0.127942	0.127942	25.73	0.000
Activity	1	0.047027	0.047027	9.46	0.003
%Fat*Weight kg	1	0.041745	0.041745	8.40	0.005
Error	87	0.432557	0.004972		
Total	91	0.988342			

Model Summary

S	R-sq	R-sq(adj)	R-sq(pred)
0.0705118	56.23%	54.22%	50.48%

Coefficients

Term	Coef	SE Coef	T-Value	P-Value	VIF
Constant	0.155	0.132	1.18	0.243	
%Fat	0.00557	0.00409	1.36	0.176	14.93
Weight kg	0.01447	0.00285	5.07	0.000	33.95
Activity	0.000022	0.000007	3.08	0.003	1.05
%Fat*Weight kg	-0.000214	0.000074	-2.90	0.005	75.06

These results show that Weight, Activity, and the interaction between them are statistically significant. The percent body fat is not statistically significant. However, the VIFs indicate that our model has severe multicollinearity for some of the independent variables.

Notice that Activity has a VIF near 1, which indicates that multicollinearity does not affect it and we can trust this coefficient and p-value with no further action. However, the coefficients and p-values for the other terms are suspect!

Additionally, at least some of the multicollinearity in our model is the structural type. We've included the interaction term of body fat * weight. Clearly, there is a correlation between the interaction term and both of the main effect terms. The VIFs reflect these relationships.

I have a neat trick to show you. There's a method to remove this type of structural multicollinearity quickly and easily!

Center the Independent Variables to Reduce Structural Multicollinearity

In our model, the interaction term is at least partially responsible for the high VIFs. Both higher-order terms and interaction terms produce multicollinearity because these terms include the main effects. Centering the variables is a simple way to reduce structural multicollinearity.

Centering the variables involves calculating the mean for each continuous independent variable and then subtracting the mean from all observed values of that variable. Then, use these centered variables in your model. Most statistical software allows you to fit your model using centered variables.

There are other standardization methods, but the advantage of just subtracting the mean is that the interpretation of the coefficients remains the same. The coefficients continue to represent the mean change in the dependent variable given a 1-unit change in the independent variable.

In the worksheet, I've included the centered independent variables in the columns with an S added to the variable names.

Regression with Centered Variables

Let's fit the same model but using the centered independent variables.

Regression Analysis: Femoral Neck versus %Fat S, Weight S, Activity S

Analysis of Variance

Source	DF	Adj SS	Adj MS	F-Value	P-Value
Regression	4	0.55578	0.138946	27.95	0.000
%Fat S	1	0.04786	0.047863	9.63	0.003
Weight S	1	0.30473	0.304728	61.29	0.000
Activity S	1	0.04703	0.047027	9.46	0.003
%Fat S*Weight S	1	0.04175	0.041745	8.40	0.005
Error	87	0.43256	0.004972		
Total	91	0.98834			

Model Summary

S	R-sq	R-sq(adj)	R-sq(pred)
0.0705118	56.23%	54.22%	50.48%

Coefficients

Term	Coef	SE Coef	T-Value	P-Value	VIF
Constant	0.82161	0.00973	84.40	0.000	
%Fat S	-0.00598	0.00193	-3.10	0.003	3.32
Weight S	0.00835	0.00107	7.83	0.000	4.75
Activity S	0.000022	0.000007	3.08	0.003	1.05
%Fat S*Weight S	-0.000214	0.000074	-2.90	0.005	1.99

The most apparent difference is that the VIFs are all down to satisfactory values; they're all less than 5. By removing the structural multicollinearity, we can see that there is some multicollinearity in our data, but it is not severe enough to warrant further corrective measures.

Removing the structural multicollinearity produced other notable differences in the output that we'll investigate.

Comparing Regression Models to Reveal Multicollinearity Effects

We can compare two versions of the same model, one with high multicollinearity and one without it. This comparison highlights its effects.

The first independent variable we'll look at is Activity. This variable was the only one to have almost no multicollinearity in the first model. Compare the Activity coefficients and p-values between the two models and you'll see that they are the same (coefficient = 0.000022, p-value = 0.003). This illustrates how only the variables that are highly correlated are affected by its problems.

Let's look at the variables that had high VIFs in the first model. The standard error of the coefficient measures the precision of the estimates. Lower values indicate more precise estimates. The standard errors in the second model are lower for both %Fat and Weight. Additionally, %Fat is significant in the second model even though it wasn't in the first model. Not only that, but the coefficient sign for %Fat has changed from positive to negative!

The lower precision, switched signs, and a lack of statistical significance are typical problems associated with multicollinearity.

Now, take a look at the Summary of Model tables for both models. You'll notice that the standard error of the regression (S), R-squared, adjusted R-squared, and predicted R-squared are all identical. As I mentioned earlier, multicollinearity doesn't affect the predictions or goodness-of-fit. If you just want to make predictions, the model with severe multicollinearity is just as good!

How to Deal with Multicollinearity

I showed how there are a variety of situations where you don't need to deal with it. The multicollinearity might not be severe, it might not affect the variables you're most interested in, or maybe you just need to make predictions. Or, perhaps it's just structural multicollinearity that you can get rid of by centering the variables.

But what if you have severe multicollinearity in your data and you find that you must deal with it? What do you do then? Unfortunately, this situation can be difficult to resolve. There are a variety of methods that you can try, but each one has some drawbacks. You'll need to use your subject-area knowledge and factor in the goals of your study to pick the solution that provides the best mix of advantages and disadvantages.

The potential solutions include the following:

- Remove some of the highly correlated independent variables.
- Linearly combine the independent variables, such as adding them together.
- Perform an analysis designed for highly correlated variables, such as principal components analysis or partial least squares regression.
- LASSO and Ridge regression are advanced forms of regression analysis that are beyond the scope of this book but they can handle multicollinearity. If you know how to perform linear least squares regression, you'll be able to handle these analyses with just a little additional study.

As you consider a solution, remember that all of these have downsides. If you can accept less precise coefficients, or a regression model with a high R-squared but hardly any statistically significant variables, then not doing anything about the multicollinearity might be the best solution.

If you are particularly interested in the estimating the effects of your independent variables, I'd recommend trying LASSO or Ridge regression. These analyses allow you specify the model as you would in OLS, and they produce estimates for all terms in your model. The other methods involve reducing your data down to fewer terms or components, which does not allow the analyses to produce estimates for all your independent variables. However, be aware that LASSO and Ridge regression introduce a small amount of bias into the estimates to reduce the variance that multicollinearity inflates.

Next Steps

Up until now, we've been looking at assumptions that apply to the dataset and residuals as a whole. Now, we'll shift gears and focus on identifying individual observations that can adversely affect the model.

Unusual Observations

In this section, I'll cover observations that have unusual values. Unfortunately, an individual observation that is unusual can have a detrimental impact on your model. Back in chapter 2, I explained how the fact that OLS uses squared residual makes it susceptible to unusual values. This problem can affect coefficients, p-values, predicted values, and R-squared. Consequently, analysts must know how to identify these problematic observations, assess their influence, and know when it is appropriate to remove observations from the model fitting process.

Observations in Regression

In regression, observations are multifaceted because each one contains a set of values for the dependent variable and all the independent variables. These values are all the properties that you measure for a single subject, item, transaction, etc., and then use in the regression model.

In a datasheet, an observation is a row of data. For example, an observation might include values for bone density for the dependent variable, and activity level and weight for the independent variable. For this model, these three values comprise an observation.

Because these observations have multiple characteristics, there are multiple ways they can be unusual. In the set of values for an observation, an individual value, or a combination of values, can cause an observation to be unusual. Furthermore, these observations fit into the larger framework of the regression model. Consequently, an observation can be unusual within the context of one model but not another.

Just because an observation is unusual doesn't necessarily indicate it has a significant impact on the model, or that it is a problem. Those are separate questions. Consequently, here's the process that we'll use to assess individual observations.

1. Identify unusual observations. "Unusual observations" is a broad term that covers several ways of being unusual.
2. Identify influential observations. Observations can be unusual, but do they have a disproportionately large impact on the model? If so, they are influential observations.
3. Determine whether influential observations are detrimental.

Unusual Observations

The first step in our process is to identify unusual observations. There are two primary modes in which an observation can be unusual—outliers and high leverage observations. Correspondingly, there are different methods for detecting them.

A key point to remember is that unusual observations are not inherently bad. Some of them don't have a negative impact on the model at all. After we identify the unusual observations, we'll need to determine if they have a detrimental influence on the model

Let's learn how observations can be unusual and how to identify them!

Outliers (Unusual Y-values)

Outlier has a very specific definition in regression analysis. Outliers are observations that don't fit the model well. For these observations, the model's descriptions of the relationships between the independent variables and the dependent variable do a poor job of predicting the observed outcome. In other words, given an observation's set of values for the independent variables, unusual observations have a particularly large difference between the predicted value and the observed value of the dependent variable. In other words, outliers are observations that have unusually large residuals. They don't fit the overall pattern of the data.

Using the bone density model (Bone Density = Activity + Weight), suppose we have observed values of A for activity level and B for weight. When we plug these values into the model equation, it predicts that bone density will be value C. If a subject's measured bone density for that observation is not close to the fitted value of C, then the model fits this observation poorly. Classification as an outlier depends on the magnitude of the residual.

Let's look at this in graphical form. We'll use an example with one independent variable (Input) and the dependent variable (Output) so we can use a fitted line plot. In the graph, most of the points follow the fitted line for the model. However, there is one point that does not fit the model.

On the graph, the circled point clearly does not fit the model well. However, you can see that the Input value (~14) for this observation isn't unusual at all because the other Input values range from 10 through 20 on the X-axis. Also, notice how the Output value (~50) is similarly within the range of values on the Y-axis (10 − 60). Neither the Input nor the Output values themselves are unusual in this dataset. Instead, it's an outlier because it doesn't fit the model. For this observation, the model predicts an Output value of approximately 35. The observed value is not close to that—which produces a large residual! It sure looks like an outlier!

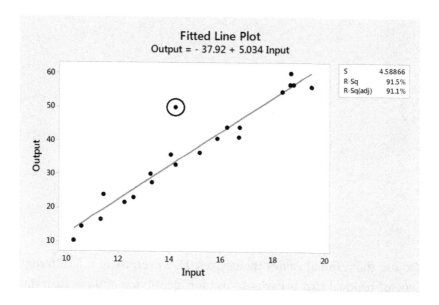

It's easy identifying this outlier using a fitted line plot because we have only one independent variable. However, when you have more than one independent variable, you can't use this plot. In that case, you can use residual plots, as shown in the residuals versus fits plot.

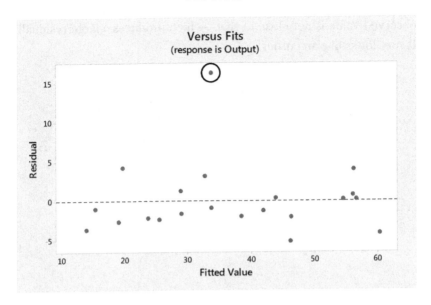

Versus Fits
(response is Output)

Or, use the residual values themselves. However, there is a different type of residual that is easier to use for identifying outliers than the raw residuals we assessed throughout this chapter. Consider that a residual of 10 might be considered small in one model but very large in another. It depends on the units of measurement, the variability in the data, and the overall fit of the model. How do you determine whether a residual of 10 is large?

It's much easier to use internally studentized residuals, also known as standardized residuals. Studentized (standardized) residuals take the raw residual value and divide it by the standard deviation of the residuals. Consequently, studentized residuals tell you how many standard deviations the observed value falls from the fitted value. For example, if the raw residual is 9 and its standard deviation is 3, the standardized residual equals 3.

When you see a studentized residual of 3, you know it's a very large residual while adjusting for your specific data and model fit.

Typically, a standardized residual of +/- 3, or more, is a common benchmark for identifying large residuals that you should investigate. These residuals are at least three standard deviations away from the predicted value. When there are no underlying problems, you'd expect approximately 1 out of every 100 observations to have standardized residuals that are at least as extreme as +/- 3. High studentized residuals don't necessarily indicate that there is a problem, but you should look into them.

The statistical software that I use (Minitab), flags residuals that have standardized residuals that are more than +/- 2 standard deviations from the fitted values. It's more cautious. Approximately 1 in 20 observations will have flagged residuals using this criterion when there are no underlying problems.

The output corresponds to the data in the previous fitted line plot. Observation 8 is the outlier in the plot. The output indicates that the raw residual (Resid) of 16.23 is 3.63 standard deviations above the mean residual.

```
Fits and Diagnostics for Unusual Observations

                              Std
Obs   Output    Fit   Resid  Resid
  8    49.89  33.66   16.23   3.63   R

R  Large residual
```

Keep in mind that flagged residuals are not necessarily problematic and it is normal to have unusual observations when there are no problems. For instance, using Minitab's criteria, you'd expect 5% of your observations to have a large standardized residual when everything is fine.

This measure helps you identify large residuals using a statistical measure. However, you need to determine whether these outliers represent a problem. We'll get to that later in this chapter.

High Leverage Observations (Unusual X-values)

As we saw, outliers have unusual Y-values. High leverage observations are unusual in a different manner. These points have an unusual value for an independent variable, or an unusual X-value. They're called leverage points because a single observation can dramatically affect the model.

Let's go back to the example bone density model from the previous section. This model has two independent variables, activity level and weight. If a subject is an elite athlete, she has an activity level that is extremely high, much higher than the other subjects. An observation of this subject is a high leverage point because it has a very unusual X-value for activity. This observation has the potential to change the model dramatically. However, having a large impact is only a possibility, not a definite.

Let's take a look at this graphically. In the graph, there is a large gap between the x-value.

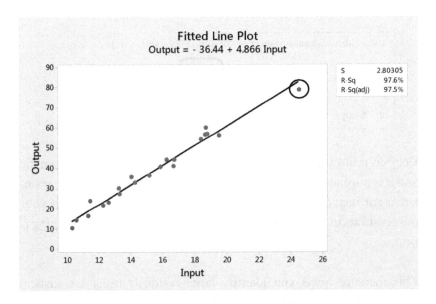

Graphs are great for detecting high leverage points. When you have one independent variable, you can use a fitted line plot, as shown in the previous graph. However, if you have more than one independent variable, you can plot each independent variable in its own histogram or boxplot, or use residual plots, to look for unusual values. The following histogram and the residual plot display the leverage point in the fitted line plot above.

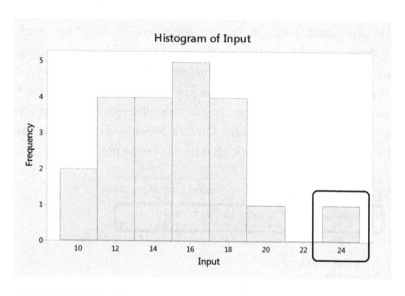

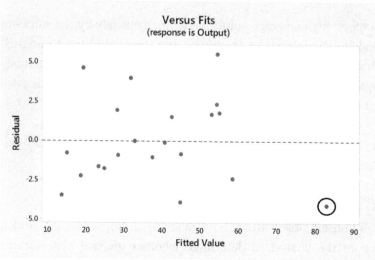

As with outliers, you can use a statistical measure to identify high leverage points— h_{ii}. This statistic represents the distance between each x-value and the mean of all x-values. These values range from 0 to 1 and add up to the number of regression coefficients plus the constant.

A common guideline states that a h_{ii} value which is greater than 3 times the average h_{ii} value represents a high leverage point that you should investigate. Fortunately, you don't need to do all this math. Your statistical software can do it for you and flag high leverage points. Minitab statistical software identifies these points as shown in the Unusual Observations table. You just need to understand what it means—it's an extreme x-value. In this case, observation 8 is the leverage point that the plot displays. Minitab does not display the h_{ii} values by default, but that's how it identifies leverage points.

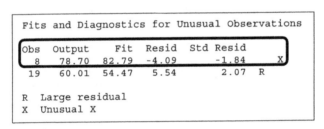

Remember, high leverage points are defined entirely by the values of the independent variables (x-values) and they only have a potential for dramatically impacting the model. Whether these points actually impact the model depends on the dependent, or Y, value that is associated with the unusual X value.

Next, we'll determine whether unusual observations are actually influential points.

Influential Points

Not all unusual observations have much of an impact on the model. It's up to the analyst to determine whether unusual observations actually affect the model greatly. If an observation does have that impact, it is an influential point.

So, how do you determine whether an unusual observation is an influential point? A simple method is to fit the model with and without the unusual observations and see how the models differ. Do the coefficients, p-values, and goodness-of-fit measures change by much?

Additionally, there are statistical measures that assess the impact that an observation has on regression models. The following are two principal measures of an observation's influence:

- **Cook's distance (D):** The distance between the coefficients calculated with and without an observation. Higher values represent more influence.
- **Difference in fits (DFITS):** Approximately the number of standard deviations that the fitted values change when an observation is removed from the dataset. Higher values represent more influence.

Your software can calculate these measures for each observation in your dataset when you fit a model. At a glance, you can see which observations are influential points. Each measure has its own guideline for when an observation is an influential point.

For Cook's distance, a D between 0.5 and 1 might be influential and it is worth investigating. D values greater than 1, or at least notably different from all other values, are extremely likely to be influential.

For difference in fits, influential points have DFITS values greater than:

$$2\sqrt{\frac{p+1}{n-p-1}}$$

Where n equals the number of observations and p equals the number of terms including the constant.

Both of these measures statistically identify influential points, but you should investigate them to be sure they impact the model. Fit the model without these points to determine how the model changes.

Instead of using Cook's distance and DFITS, I'll usually just fit the model with and without outliers and high leverage points to see how the models compare. That approach lets me assess the differences between the models rather than relying solely on the statistical measures of influence. If you use the statistical method for identifying influential points (Cook's and DFITS), you'll still need to perform that model comparison.

You know how to identify unusual observations and how to determine whether they are influential points. Next, I'll give you some guidelines and tips for managing these points when you find them!

Managing Unusual Observations and Influential Points

The process we're following is to first identify unusual observations, and then determine whether they are influential points. Now, we'll determine whether any of these are problematic. You might need to remove problematic observations from the model. This part of the process usually involves subject-area knowledge and double-checking data more than statistical measures. The statistical measures can tell you whether an observation is unusual and influential—but not whether you should remove them from the model.

Let's first look at the easy things you can check. When you have unusual observations, it's always a good idea to check for data entry errors and all other potential problems with the data in your datasheet. When you perform enough analyses, these errors will crop up at some point. A number might be entered incorrectly. Or the values can be entered on the wrong row.

After you verify that the data are correct, you should determine whether an unusual observation is an influential point. Before you get too wrapped up in a hairy debate about removing an observation, determine whether it's an influential point. If an unusual observation has only a small impact on the model, determining whether you should remove it becomes much less critical. The results are substantially the same either way. However, if an observation is truly unusual and influential, you'll need to start asking other types of questions.

Researchers often feel like they need to remove influential observations from the dataset. However, while that can improve the fit of the data, it's not always a good idea. You're throwing out potentially valuable information and, in the process, potentially biasing the results and inflating the appearance of the model's explanatory power.

To determine whether to remove an observation, you'll need to assess if it appropriately reflects your target population, subject-area, research question, and research methodology. Did anything unusual happen while measuring these observations, such as power failures, unusual experimental conditions, or anything else out of the norm? Is there anything substantially different about the subject being observed whether it's a person, item, or transaction? Did measurement error occur?

For example, in the bone density study I participated in, I noticed an outlier in the bone density model. The model didn't predict her bone density well at all. The study's subject coordinator reminded me that the subject has diabetes, which affects bone health. The goal of our study was to model bone density in subjects with normal bone growth. Consequently, her data were excluded from our analyses because she was not a member of our target population. While we excluded her data, we retained her as subject because many of her classmates were participating in the study and we didn't want her to feel left out!

Conversely, a point can be unusual and influential, but if there's no identifiable reason to exclude it, it might be best to leave it in the model. It might capture valuable information that is part of your study area. Leaving these points in can be hard, particularly when it significantly reduces the model's goodness-of-fit!

For example, I fit a model that uses historical U.S. Presidential approval ratings to predict how later historians would ultimately rank each President. It turns out a President's lowest approval ratings predicts the historian ranks. However, one data point severally affects the model. President Truman doesn't fit the model because he had very low approval ratings while he was President, but later historians give him a fairly good rank of #6. If I remove that single observation, the R-squared increases by over 30 percentage points!

However, there was no justifiable reason to remove that point. While it was an oddball, it accurately reflects the potential surprises and uncertainty inherent in the political system. If I remove it, the model makes the process appear more predictable than it actually is. Even though this unusual observation is influential, I left it in the model. It's bad practice to remove data points simply to produce a better fitting model.

If you decided to remove observations, be sure to document the excluded data points and explain your reasoning. Another approach is to fit the model with and without these observations and discuss the differences. Comparing models in this manner is particularly useful when you're unsure about removing an observation and when there is substantial disagreement within a group over this question.

Next Steps

You've seen how different problems with your model can manifest themselves in the residuals. Next, I'll show you a solution that can fix a number of these problems.

Using Data Transformations to Fix Problems

In this section, I focus on a potential solution for several problems in this chapter—data transformations. However, use this solution as the last resort. I've presented other methods for solving these problems, and you should try those first. If those methods don't work, consider transforming your data.

Data transformations take the values for a continuous variable, applies a function to each value, and converts the entire set of values for the variable into a different set of numbers. Analysts transform data that do not satisfy the assumptions of an analysis in the hopes that the converted data will meet the assumptions—such as transforming a dataset so it follows a normal distribution. Then, the analyst fits a model to the transformed data rather than the original data. There are a variety of transformation functions you can use, such as using the square root, logarithm, power, reciprocal or arcsine. The choice depends on your goals and the properties of the data.

For example, the most common transformation is probably the natural log—which is denoted as log or ln. Here's how it works. The natural log is e^x, where e equals ~2.718. When transforming your data using the natural log, the software calculates the power by which to raise 2.718 that produces the original value. The power becomes the transformed value for that original value. Suppose the original value is 10. Your software calculates X in the following: $2.718^X = 10$. In this case, X is the new data point, and it equals 2.302585093 because $2.718^{2.302585093} = 10$. The software repeats this process for all values of a variable.

Taking the square root is another common transformation. For example, if your original data point is 9, the square root transformed value is 3.

In regression, you generally assess assumptions using residual plots. Consequently, you'll often use transformations to make unruly residual plots behave! Consider using data transformations when your residual plots display curved patterns, nonconstant variance, or a nonnormal distribution. However, for reasons that I discuss later, use transformations as the solution of last resort.

As an analyst, the process starts by assessing your residual plots and identifying the problem in your model. After doing that, there are several key questions you must answer. Which variables will you transform? And, which transformation will you use? Answering these questions is trial by error to some extent. Like much of the model fitting process, it is an iterative process. Try one transformation on a variable, fit the model, check the residual plots, and then try another transformation or another variable if necessary.

Determining which Variables to Transform

While trial and error are part of the process, understanding the problem can help you narrow down which variables to transform and which transformations to use. You can transform only continuous variables.

Only Independent variable(s): When the model doesn't correctly fit the curvature, the residual plots displays curved patterns. Transforming the independent variable associated with the curvature is a potential solution. To identify which independent variable to transform, plot the residuals by each variable and look for curved patterns. Transformations of the independent variables allow you to model nonlinear relationships that you could not otherwise model using linear regression. I'm using "nonlinear" in the strict statistical sense rather than just any type of curved relationship. I showed an example of using a natural log transformation in Chapter 4.

Only the dependent variable: If your residuals do not follow the normal distribution or do not have a constant variance, transforming the dependent variable might fix the problem. Earlier in this chapter, I went through an example of using a transformation to correct non-constant variance (heteroscedasticity). Additionally, consider transforming your dependent variable when it covers a broad range of values that extend over several orders of magnitude, or it follows a very nonnormal distribution.

Both the dependent and independent variables: If you have nonlinear relationships along with nonnormal residuals or residuals with non-constant variance, you might need to transform both the dependent and independent variables. In other words, there's just a lot wrong with the model! In chapter 13, I discuss log-log plots and present an example, which transforms both the dependent and independent variables.

Determining which Transformation to Use

Again, it might require some trial and error because the following guidelines don't always produce the best result. The first step is to determine what other studies have done. Perhaps other researchers have already found a good solution for similar data? If so, that is a good starting point!

If your residuals are not normal or have unequal variances, try a power transformation of the dependent variable. These transformations involve raising your data points to a power denoted by lambda (λ). In other words, the transformed values equal y^{λ}. More on these power transformations shortly!

For unequal variances, the natural log, which is one of the power transformations, and the reciprocal ($1/Y$) are good ones to try.

Fortunately, there are several tools you can use to help identify the best transformation. Both the Box-Cox transformation and Johnson transformation assess families of transformations and attempts to determine the best one for your data. These tools can really help you out when you don't know which transformation to use!

Box-Cox Transformation

The Box-Cox transformation assesses a family of power transformations on Y where the exponent lambda (λ) can range between -5 and 5. The procedure identifies the optimal power by which to raise your raw data for Y. You cannot use the Box-Cox transformation when your data contain zero or negative values.

While lambda can be any value in the range, some values are more intuitive to understand, as shown in the table.

Lambda (λ)	Transformation
2	Y squared
0.5	Square root of Y
0	Natural log of Y
-0.5	1 / square root Y
-1	1 / Y

Johnson Transformation

The Johnson transformation uses a different algorithm than the Box-Cox transformation. This transformation function selects from three families of functions by changing their parameters. It is a more powerful transformation than the Box-Cox transformation, and it can usually find an acceptable transformation. Additionally, you can use the Johnson transformation when your data have zero or negative values.

While this transformation is powerful, it is also less intuitive. Typically, I suggest using the Box-Cox transformation first. If that fails to produce a good transformation, then try the Johnson transformation.

How to Interpret the Results for Transformed Data

When you transform the data and fit a model, the statistical results apply to the transformed data rather than the original data. You describe the relationship as you would for untransformed data but including information about the transformed variable(s).

For example, if there is a positive relationship between Input and Output, but you used a natural log transformation on Output, you'd state that there is a positive, linear relationship between Input and the natural log of the Output. In other words, as Input increases, the expected natural log of the Output also increases.

If you transformed both Input and Output, you state that there is a positive, linear relationship between the natural log of Input and the natural log of the Output.

In that manner, some aspects of the interpretation remain similar. However, be aware that the coefficients, predictions, and prediction intervals all correspond to the transformed data. If you graph the results on a fitted line plot, the line follows the transformed data. Interpreting the results is less intuitive! Even the graph, which usually brings that data to life, won't look anything like the real data! For an example, see the log-log plot in chapter 13.

You can manually back transform the values (coefficients, predictions, etc.) to obtain them in their natural units. Alternatively, some statistical software can back convert the values for you automatically. While this is convenient, I always find that it still requires extra work to understand what the relationships really look like. Plot the raw data in scatterplots to see the untransformed relationships. It can be eye-opening!

For example, sometimes the transformed relationships appear like nice, consistently tight linear fits. However, when you graph the raw data, it can be entirely different—such as being sharply curved with a dramatically varying tightness of the fit! If you need to transform your data, take the extra effort to gain a deep understanding of the relationship in natural units.

Additionally, if you transform the dependent variable, it changes the variance structure of the Y-variable and the residuals. Goodness-of-fit statistics, such as R-squared and the standard error of the regression (S), apply to the transformed data rather than the raw data. Additionally, you can't compare these statistics between models with untransformed and transformed dependent variables. Furthermore, the standard error of the mean is in the units of the transformed variable rather than natural units. You can't back transform S because it is likely to change over the range of the fitted values.

Use data transformation as a last resort!

Because of these added interpretation difficulties, use transformations as a last resort. If your residuals have curved patterns, are nonnormal, or have nonconstant variance, you can use various techniques to resolve the problem. Methods other than data transformations are generally better because they involve specifying a better form of the model, such as including an important variable or fitting curvature, which fixes the underlying problem. Transforming the data without addressing underlying specification errors is akin to sweeping the problem beneath the carpet. The underlying problem remains even though the residuals look nice!

Don't get me wrong, in some cases transforming your data is the best option. It can help you out. However, only use it when nothing else works!

Cheat Sheet for Detecting and Solving Problems

Throughout this chapter, you've learned about various assumption violations and other issues that can produce results you can't trust. Here's a cheat sheet to help you navigate the numerous problems, detection methods, and corrective measures!

OLS Potential Problem	Assessment	Possible solutions
Model does not adequately fit curvature in data.	Curved patterns in residuals vs variables plot	Use polynomials or inverses to fit curves using OLS
		Use Nonlinear regression to fit a wider variety of curves
		Data transformation (e.g., log)
Heteroscedasticity: Residuals do not have a constant variance	Fan shape in residuals vs fits plot	Redefine IVs to focus on rates, per capita, etc. rather than raw measure
		Weighted least squares
		Data transformation

OLS Potential Problem	Assessment	Possible solutions
Autocorrelation: Residuals are correlated with adjacent residuals	Patterns in residuals vs order plot	Add lag variable, which are past values of the IVs
	Durbin-Watson statistic	Add independent variable to include time information
		Time series analysis
Residuals do not follow normal distribution	Normal plot of residuals	Specify correct model
	Histogram	Check for outliers
	Normality test	Use Generalized Linear Models (GLM) regression which allows for other error distributions
		Data transformation and then use OLS

OLS Potential Problem	Assessment	Possible solutions
Individual observations that are unusual and strongly influence the model	Residual plots Fit model with and without observations to observe how it affects model estimates DFITS Cook's distance Leverages	Remove unusual observations when they don't reflect your study area. Or, include model with and without observations in your report and discuss.
Multicollinearity: Independent variables are correlated	Variance inflation factors (VIF) greater than 5 Coefficients with unexpected signs	Remove independent variable Linear combination of variables Use PLS, LASSO, or Ridge regression

CHAPTER 10

Using Regression to Make Predictions

So far, you've learned how to specify a regression model, check the residuals and assumptions, and identify and fix problems. You also know how to interpret the results so you can describe the relationships between the independent variables and the dependent variable. Now, we'll go into another use for regression analysis—making predictions.

If you were able to make predictions about something important to you, you'd probably love that, right? It's even better if you know that your predictions are sound. In this section, I show how to use regression analysis to make predictions and determine whether they are both unbiased and precise.

You can use regression equations to make predictions. Regression equations are a crucial part of the statistical output after you fit a model. As you saw earlier, the coefficients in the equation define the relationship between each independent variable and the dependent variable. However, you can also enter values for the independent variables into the equation to predict the mean value of the dependent variable.

Unfortunately, as you'll see, predictions are not as simple as entering values into an equation and obtaining a single number for the prediction. You need to assess both precision and bias.

Explanatory versus Predictive Models

Most of this book focuses on using regression to understand and describe the relationships between each of your independent variables and the dependent variable from a scientific standpoint. Is there a relationship between X and Y? If so, what is the nature of that relationship? These are explanatory models.

Explanatory model building attempts to devise a scientific explanation for a phenomenon. The goal is to develop a model that contains scientifically essential variables that are theoretically relevant, statistically significant, and to estimate their effect sizes. Additionally, statisticians can use an explanatory model to test a particular hypothesis that a study is assessing.

For example, what variables correlate to bone density? In this context, does an exercise intervention significantly increase bone density? If so, what is the average bone density increase?

Predictive models try to produce the most precise and unbiased predictions possible. I'll discuss these concepts at length in this chapter. For these types of models, analysts pay much less attention to the nature of the relationships between the independent variables and the dependent variable. You only want good predictions, which changes how you build your model and how you assess it.

With these goals in mind, including theoretically important variables takes a back seat. Sure, building an explanatory model and a predictive model will likely use a common subset of variables that do make theoretical sense. However, predictive models can include variables that don't make sense theoretically as long as it improves the quality of the predictions. These variables might include some that are not causally correlated with the dependent variable.

For a silly example, if ice cream sales in a beach town correlate with shark attacks, ice cream parlors might want to include shark attacks in their models!

Conversely, analysts don't need to include theoretically important independent variables if they don't improve the predictions. For example, the ratio of men to women visitors might predict the amount of ice cream sales. If this variable is statistically significant, but it does not improve the predictions, analysts can remove it from a predictive model.

When you fit a predictive model, it frees you up a bit because you're not tied down to only theoretically important variables. That can open up many possibilities. However, there are different constraints and priorities for predictive models. For instance, predictor variables must be measurable quickly. If you can't measure a variable early enough, you can't use it to make predictions!

Typically, predictive models require data that are easy and inexpensive to obtain. If you regularly predict an outcome (e.g., weekly sales), you don't want the values of the predictors to be a burden to obtain before plugging them into the regression model! The cost and ease of collecting the necessary information to generate the predictions are often top-priorities.

For example, the hypothetical predictor variable of the ratio of men to women visitors in the beach town might be a burden to collect. You'll need to pay a researcher to regularly observe a random sample of visitors and calculate this ratio for each prediction. That might be a problem! If there is an easier way to obtain similar information, you might use that instead.

Finally, while chasing a high R-squared is always a temptation, it is even more so for predictive models. As you learned in the goodness-of-fit chapter, a high R-squared is not always important, but it is for predictive models. Consequently, in predictive models, analysts often chase the most precise prediction but must be wary of overfitting the model in the process. As chapter 8 shows, overfit models explain the quirks of your dataset, but they don't generalize well beyond that dataset. That's a show stopper for useful predictions!

The Regression Approach for Predictions

Using regression to make predictions doesn't necessarily involve predicting the future. Instead, you predict the mean of the dependent variable given specific values of the independent variable(s). For our example, we'll use one independent variable to predict the dependent variable. I measured both of these variables at the same point in time.

Psychic predictions are things that just pop into mind and are not often verified against reality. Unsurprisingly, predictions in the regression context are more rigorous. We need to collect data for relevant variables, formulate a model, and evaluate how well the model fits the data.

The general procedure for using regression to make good predictions is the following:

1. Research the subject-area so you can build on the work of others. This research helps with the subsequent steps.
2. Collect data for the relevant variables.
3. Specify and assess your regression model.
4. If you have a model that adequately fits the data, use it to make predictions.

While this process involves more work than the psychic approach, it provides valuable benefits. With regression, we can evaluate the bias and precision of our predictions:

- Bias in a statistical model indicates that the predictions are systematically too high or too low.
- Precision represents how close the predictions are to the observed values.

When we use regression to make predictions, our goal is to produce predictions that are both correct on average and close to the real values. In other words, we need predictions that are both unbiased and precise.

Example Scenario for Regression Predictions

We'll use a regression model to predict body fat percentage based on body mass index (BMI). I collected these data for a study with 92 middle school girls. The variables we measured include height, weight, and body fat measured by a Hologic DXA whole-body system. I've calculated the BMI using the height and weight measurements. DXA measurements of body fat percentage are considered to be among the best.

Use this CSV data file: Predict_BMI.

Why might we want to use BMI to predict body fat percentage? It's more expensive to obtain your body fat percentage through a direct measure like DXA. If you can use your BMI to predict your body fat percentage, that provides valuable information more easily and cheaply. Let's see if BMI can produce good predictions!

Finding a Good Regression Model for Predictions

We have the data. Now, we need to determine whether there is a statistically significant relationship between the variables. Relationships, or correlations between variables, are crucial if we want to use the value of one variable to predict the value of another. We also need to evaluate the suitability of the regression model for making predictions.

We have only one independent variable (BMI), so we can use a fitted line plot to display its relationship with body fat percentage. The relationship between the variables is curvilinear. I'll use a polynomial term to fit the curvature. In this case, I'll include a quadratic (squared) term. The fitted line plot suggests that this model fits the data.

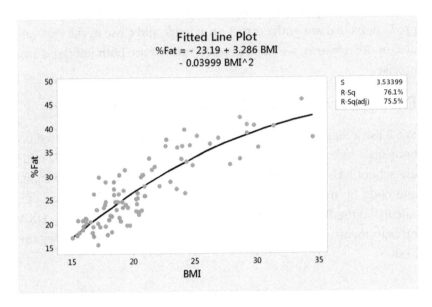

This curvature is readily apparent because we have only one independent variable and we can graph the relationship. If your model has more than one independent variable, use separate scatterplots to display the association between each independent variable and the dependent variable so you can evaluate the nature of each relationship.

Assess the Residual Plots

You should also assess the residual plots. If you see patterns in the residual plots, you know that your model is incorrect and that you need to reevaluate it.

The residual plots confirm the unbiased fit because the data points fall randomly around zero and follow a normal distribution.

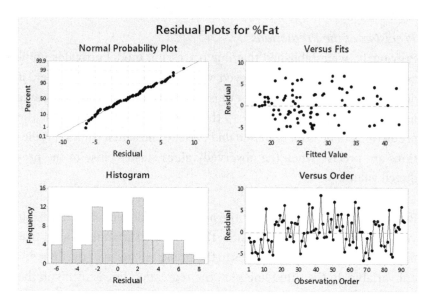

Interpret the Regression Output

In the statistical output below, the p-values indicate that both the linear and squared terms are statistically significant. Based on all of this information, we have a model that provides a statistically significant and unbiased fit to these data. We have a valid regression model. However, there are additional issues we must consider before we can use this model to make predictions.

```
Sequential Analysis of Variance

Source       DF      SS        F       P
Linear        1   3454.62   261.65   0.000
Quadratic     1     76.75     6.15   0.015
```

As an aside, the curved relationship is interesting. The flattening curve indicates that higher BMI values are associated with smaller increases in body fat percentage.

Other Considerations for Valid Predictions

Precision of the Predictions

Previously, we established that our regression model provides unbiased predictions of the observed values. That's good. However, it doesn't address the precision of those predictions. Precision measures how close the predictions are to the observed values. We want the predictions to be both unbiased *and* close to the actual values. Predictions are precise when the observed values cluster close to the predicted values.

Regression predictions are for the *mean* of the dependent variable. If you think of any mean, you know that there is variation around that mean. The same concept applies to the predicted mean of the dependent variable. In the fitted line plot, the regression line is nicely in the center of the data points. However, there is a spread of data points around the line. We need to quantify that scatter to know how close the predictions are to the observed values. If the range is too large, the predictions won't provide useful information.

Later, I'll generate predictions and show you how to assess the precision.

Goodness-of-Fit Measures

We covered various goodness-of-fit measures earlier, but now I'll revisit them in the context of making predictions.

Goodness-of-fit measures, like R-squared, assess the scatter of the data points around the fitted value. The R-squared for our model is 76.1%, which is good but not great. For a given dataset, higher R-squared values represent predictions that are more precise. However, R-squared doesn't tell us directly how precise the predictions are in the units of the dependent variable. We can use the standard error of the regression (S) to assess the precision in this manner. The predicted value plus/minus 2*S is a quick estimate of a 95% prediction interval. However, for this section, I'll use prediction intervals to evaluate precision.

New Observations versus Data Used to Fit the Model

R-squared and S indicate how well the model fits the observed data. We need predictions for new observations that the analysis did not use during the model estimation process. Assessing that type of fit requires a different goodness-of-fit measure, the predicted R-squared.

Even when a regression model has a high R-squared value, it might not be able to predict new observations as well. Use predicted R-squared to evaluate how well your model predicts the value of new observations. Statistical software packages calculate it by sequentially removing each observation, fitting the model, and determining how well the model predicts the removed observations.

If the predicted R-squared is much lower than the regular R-squared, you know that your regression model doesn't predict new observations as well as it fits the current dataset. This situation should make you wary of the predictions.

The Model Summary table indicates that the predicted R-squared (74.14%) is nearly equal to the regular R-squared (76.06%) for our model. We have reason to believe that the model predicts new observations nearly as well as it fits the dataset.

```
Model Summary

       S    R-sq  R-sq(adj)  R-sq(pred)
 3.53399  76.06%     75.52%      74.14%
```

Make Predictions Only Within the Range of the Data

Regression predictions are valid only for the range of data used to estimate the model. The relationship between the independent variables and the dependent variable can change outside of that range. In other words, we don't know whether the shape of the curve changes. If it does, our predictions will be invalid.

The graph shows that the observed BMI values range from 15-35. We should not make predictions outside of this range.

Make Predictions Only for the Population You Sampled

The relationships that a regression model estimates might be valid for only the specific population that you sampled. Our data were collected from middle school girls that are 12-14 years old. The relationship between BMI and body fat percentage might be different for males and different age groups.

Using our Regression Model to Make Predictions

We have a valid regression model that appears to produce unbiased predictions and can predict new observations nearly as well as it predicts the data used to fit the model. Let's go ahead and use our model to make a prediction and assess the precision.

It is possible to use the regression equation and calculate the predicted values ourselves. However, I'll use statistical software to do this for us. Not only is this approach easier and more accurate, but I'll also have it calculate the prediction intervals so we can assess the precision.

I'll use the software to predict the body fat percentage for a BMI of 18.

```
Prediction for %Fat

Regression Equation

%Fat = -23.19 + 3.286 BMI - 0.0400 BMI*BMI

Variable Setting
BMI          18

    Fit    SE Fit      95% CI              95% PI
22.9994  0.437448  (22.1302, 23.8686)  (15.9239, 30.0750)
```

Interpreting the Regression Prediction Results

The output indicates that the mean value associated with a BMI of 18 is estimated to be ~23% body fat. Again, this mean applies to the population of middle school girls. Let's assess the precision using the confidence interval (CI) and the prediction interval (PI).

The confidence interval of the prediction is the range that is likely to contain the mean body fat percentage for the population of girls with a BMI of 18. We can be 95% confident that this mean is between 22.1% and 23.9%. However, this confidence interval does not help us evaluate the precision of individual predictions.

A prediction interval (PI) is the range where a single new observation is likely to fall given specific values of the independent variables. Prediction intervals factor in the variability around the mean outcome and represent a margin of error around the fitted value. Narrower prediction intervals represent more precise predictions because they have a smaller margin of error. Use prediction intervals to determine whether the predictions are sufficiently precise to satisfy your requirements.

Prediction intervals have a confidence level and can be a two-sided range or be an upper or lower bound. Let's see how prediction intervals can help us!

From the prediction output, we can be 95% confident that an individual middle school girl with a BMI of 18 will have body fat percentage between 16% and 30%.

The range of the prediction interval is always wider than the confidence interval of the mean due to the greater uncertainty of predicting an individual value.

Is this prediction sufficiently precise? To make this determination, we'll need to use our subject-area knowledge in conjunction with any specific requirements we have. I'm not a medical expert, but I'd guess that the 14-point range of 16-30% is too imprecise to provide meaningful information. If this is true, our regression model is too imprecise to be useful.

Next Steps: Don't Focus On Only the Fitted Values

Using regression analysis to make predictions is a multi-step process. After collecting the data, you need to specify a valid model. The model must satisfy several conditions before you make predictions. Finally, be sure to assess the precision of the predictions. Unfortunately, it's all too easy to be fooled by the apparent precision of plugging values into an equation and calculating an exact answer. As you saw, there is a margin of error around the predictions, which you must factor into your usage of them.

Let's dig deeper into the precision of the predictions.

The Illusion of Predictability

As we saw in the previous section, the precision of the predictions refers to how close the model's predictions are to the observed values. The more precise the model, the closer the data points are to the predictions. When you have an imprecise model, the observations tend to be further away from the predictions, thereby reducing the usefulness of the predictions. If you have a model that is not sufficiently precise, you risk making costly mistakes!

Regression models are a critical part of predictive analytics. These models can help you make predictions in applied situations. By entering values into the regression equation, you can predict the average outcome. However, predictions are not quite this simple because you need to understand the precision.

In this section, I present research that shows how surprisingly easy it is for even statistical experts to make mistakes related to misunderstanding the precision of the predictions. The research shows that how analysts present regression results influences the probability of making a wrong decision. I'll show you a variety of potential solutions so you can avoid these traps!

Emre Soyer and Robin M. Hogarth study behavioral decision-making. They found that experts in applied regression analysis frequently make incorrect decisions based on applied regression models because they misinterpret the prediction precision. (Soyer & Hogarth, 2012)

Decision-makers can use regression equations for predictive analytics. However, predictions are not as straightforward as entering numbers into an equation and making a decision based on the particular value of the prediction. Instead, decisions based on regression predictions need to incorporate the margin of error around the predicted value.

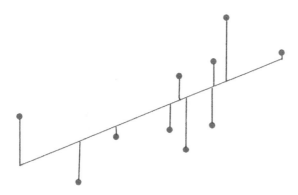

As precision increases, the data points move closer to the regression line.

Soyer and Hogarth conclude that analysts frequently perceive the outcomes to be more predictable than the model justifies. The apparent simplicity of inputting numbers into a regression equation and obtaining a particular prediction frequently deceives the analysts into believing that the value is an exact estimate. It *seems* like the regression equation is giving you the correct answer exactly, but it's not. Soyer and Hogarth call this phenomenon the illusion of predictability.

I'll show you this illusion in action, and then present some ways to mitigate its effect.

Studying How Experts Perceive Prediction Uncertainty

Soyer and Hogarth recruited 257 economists and asked them to assess regression results and use them to make a decision. Many empirical economic studies use regression models, so this is familiar territory for economists.

The researchers displayed the regression output using the most common tabular format that appears in the top economic journals: descriptive statistics, regression coefficients, constant, standard errors, R-squared, and the number of observations. Then, they asked the participants to make a decision using the model. The participants are mainly professors in applied economics and econometrics. Here's an example.

Use a Regression Model to Make a Decision

To be sure that you have a 95% probability of obtaining a positive outcome ($Y > 0$), what is the minimum value of X that you need?

The regression coefficient is statistically significant at the 95% level, and standard errors are in parentheses.

Variable	Mean	Std. Dev
X	50.72	28.12
Y	51.11	40.78

X Coefficient	1.001 (0.033)
Constant	0.32 (1.92)
R-squared	0.50
N	1000

The Difference between Perception and Reality

76% of the participants indicated that a very small X (X < 10) is sufficient to ensure a 95% probability of a positive Y.

Let's work through their logic using the regression equation that you can construct from the information in the table: $Y = 0.32 + 1.001X$.

If you enter a value of 10 in the equation for X, you obtain a predicted Y of 10.33. This prediction seems sufficiently above zero to virtually assure a positive outcome, right? The predicted value is the average outcome, but it doesn't factor in the precision of the predictions around the mean.

When you factor in the variability around the average outcome, you find that the correct answer is 47! Unfortunately, only 20% of the experts gave an answer that was near the correct value even though it is possible to solve it mathematically using the information in the table. (These are experts, after all, and I wouldn't expect most people to be able to solve it mathematically. I'll cover easier methods.)

Imagine if an important decision depended on this answer? That's how costly mistakes can be made!

Low R-squared Values Should Have Warned of Low Precision

The researchers asked the same question for a model with an R-squared of 25%, and the results were essentially the same. No changes were made in their answers to address the greater uncertainty!

The participants severely overestimated the precision of the regression predictions. Again, this is the illusion of predictability. It's a psychological phenomenon where the apparent exactness of the regression equation gives the impression that the predictions are more precise than they are in reality. The end result is that a majority of experts severely underestimated the variability, which can lead to expensive mistakes. If the numeric results deceive most applied regression *experts*, imagine how common this mistake must be among less experienced analysts!

I've written that a high R-squared value isn't always critical *except* for when you require precise predictions. In the first model, the R-squared of 50% should have set off alarm bells about imprecise predictions. Even more so for the model with an R-squared of 25%! Later in this section, we'll revisit prediction intervals and see how they can help.

Graph the Model to Highlight the Variability

In the next phase of the experiment, the researchers ask two new groups of experts the same questions about the same models, but they present the regression results differently. One group saw the results tables with fitted line plots, and the other group saw only the fitted line plots. Fitted line plots display both the data points and the fitted regression line. Surprisingly, the group that saw only the fitted line plots had the largest percentage of correct answers.

The fitted line plot represents the same R-squared = 50% model that produced the regression results in the previous tables.

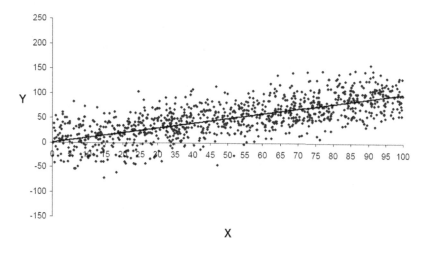

By assessing the fitted line plot, only 10% answered with an X < 10 while 66% were close to 47. Look at the graph, and it's easy to see that at around 47 most of the data points are greater than zero. You can also understand why answers of X < 10 are way off!

The graph brings the imprecision of the predictions to life. You see the variability of the data points around the fitted line.

Graphs Are One Way to Pierce the Illusion of Predictability

I completely agree with Soyer and Hogarth's call to change how analysts present the results for predictive analytics. I use fitted line plots frequently. It's a fantastic tool that makes regression results more intuitive. Seeing is believing!

However, the scenario that the researchers present is especially favorable to a visual analysis. For a start, there is only one independent variable, which allows you to use a fitted line graph. Furthermore, there are many data points (N = 1000) that are evenly distributed throughout the full range of both variables. Collectively, this situation produces a clearly visible location on the graph where you are unlikely to obtain negative values.

What do you do when you have multiple independent variables and can't use a fitted line plot? What about models that have interaction and polynomial terms? How about cases where you don't have such a large amount of nicely arranged data? For these messier but more common cases, we must still factor in the real-world variability to understand the precision in predictive analytics. Read on!

Display Prediction Intervals on Fitted Line Plots to Assess Precision

I've created a dataset that is very similar to the data that Soyer and Hogarth use for their study. Use this CSV data file to try it yourself: SimpleRegressionPrecision.

Let's start out with a simple case by using prediction intervals to answer the same question they asked in their study. Then, we'll look at several more complex cases.

What is the minimum value of X that ensures a positive result (Y > 0) with 95% probability?

To choose the correct value, we need a 95% lower bound for the prediction, which is a one-sided prediction interval with a 95% confidence level. Unfortunately, the software I'm using can't display a one-sided prediction interval on a fitted line plot, but the lower limit of a two-sided 90% prediction interval is equivalent to a 95% lower bound. Consequently, on the fitted line plot, we'll use only the lower prediction interval line.

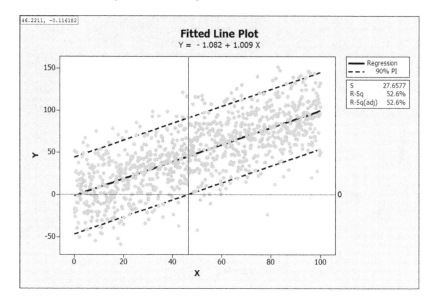

In the plot, I placed the crosshairs over the point where the 95% lower bound crosses zero on the y-axis. The software displays the values for this point in the upper-left corner of the graph. The results tell us that we need an X of just over 46.2211 to obtain a Y greater than zero with 95% confidence.

As I noted earlier, this dataset is particularly conducive to visual analysis. What if we have fewer data points that aren't so consistently arranged?

I randomly sampled 50 observations from the complete data set and created the following fitted line plot.

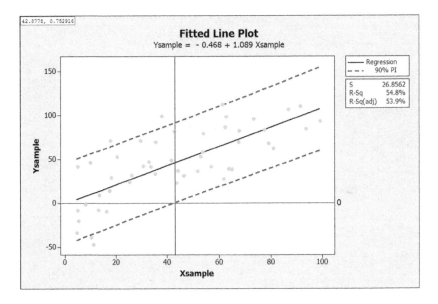

With this dataset, it's hard to determine the answer visually. Prediction intervals really shine here. Even though the sample is only 1/20th the size of the full dataset, the results are very close. Using the crosshairs again, we see that the answer is 42.8778.

Different Example of Using Prediction Intervals

The previous models have only one independent variable, which allowed us to graph the model and the prediction intervals. If you have more than one independent variable, you can't graph prediction intervals, but you can still use them.

We'll use a regression model to decide how to set the pressure and fuel flow in our process. These variables predict the heat that the process generates. Use this CSV data file to try it yourself: MultipleRegressionPrecision. The regression output follows.

```
Model Summary

      S    R-sq  R-sq(adj)  R-sq(pred)
8.93207  85.87%     84.78%      81.36%


Coefficients

Term          Coef  SE Coef  T-Value  P-Value   VIF
Constant     483.7     39.6    12.22    0.000
Pressure     4.796    0.951     5.04    0.000  1.09
Fuel Rate   -24.22     1.94   -12.48    0.000  1.09


Regression Equation

Temperature = 483.7 + 4.796 Pressure - 24.22 Fuel Rate
```

To prevent equipment damage, we must avoid excessive heat. We need to set the pressure and fuel flow so that we can be 95% confident that the heat will be less than 250. However, we don't want to go too low because it reduces the efficiency of the system.

We could plug numbers into the regression equation to find values that produce an average heat of 250. However, we know that there will be variation around this average. Consequently, we'll need to set the pressure and fuel flow to produce an average that is somewhat less than 250. How much lower is sufficient? We'll use prediction intervals to find out!

Finding the correct settings to use for pressure and fuel flow requires subject-area knowledge to determine settings that are both feasible and will produce temperatures in the right ballpark. Using a combination of experience and trial and error, you want to produce results where the 95% upper bound is near 250.

Most statistical software allows you to create prediction intervals based on a regression model. While the process varies by statistical software package, I'm using Minitab, and I show how I enter the settings and the results that it calculates. It's convenient because the software calculates the mean outcome and the prediction interval using the regression model that you fit. I'm entering process settings of 36 for pressure and 17.5 for fuel flow. I've also set it so that the software will calculate a 95% upper bound.

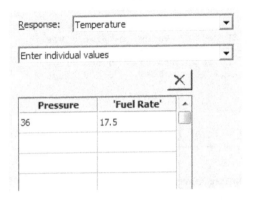

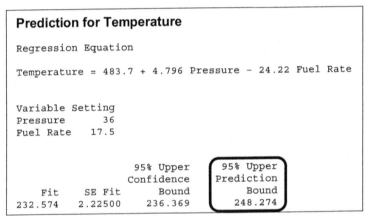

Prediction for Temperature

Regression Equation

Temperature = 483.7 + 4.796 Pressure - 24.22 Fuel Rate

Variable Setting
Pressure   36
Fuel Rate   17.5

		95% Upper Confidence	95% Upper Prediction
Fit	SE Fit	Bound	Bound
232.574	2.22500	236.369	248.274

The output shows that if we set the pressure and fuel flow at 36 and 17.5 respectively, the average temperature is 232.574 and the upper bound is 248.274. We can be 95% confident that the next temperature measurement at these settings will be below 248. That's just what we need! We're using the prediction interval to show us the precision of the predictions to incorporate the process's inherent variability into our decision-making.

We can use this same procedure even when our regression model includes more independent variables, curvature, and interaction terms.

After using regression analysis and the prediction intervals to identify candidate settings, perform validation runs at these settings to be sure that the real world behaves as your model predicts it should!

CHAPTER 11

Tips, Common Questions, and Concerns

Over the many years that I've been helping people with statistics, some common questions and concerns have emerged. In this chapter, I address some of them. Many of these topics touch on ideas that I've discussed earlier in this book but I approach them from a different angle. Some of these simply reinforce what I've written earlier.

In this chapter, I'll help you understand what an excellent regression-based study looks like. I'll show you how to identify the most important variables in a regression model, and explain why that isn't as straightforward as you might expect. Then, I address several issues related to R-squared. There's always seems to be so many questions about that statistic! How high does R-squared need to be? Is mine too high? Too low? And, what does it mean if my model has significant variables, but the R-squared is low?

Five Tips to Avoid Common Problems

Why use regression at all? What are common problems that trip up analysts? And, how do you differentiate a high-quality regression analysis from a less rigorous study?

Regression is a very powerful statistical analysis. It allows you to isolate and understand the effects of individual variables, model curvature and interactions, and make predictions. Regression analysis offers high flexibility but presents a variety of potential pitfalls. Great power requires great responsibility!

Here are five tips that will not only help you avoid common problems but also make the modeling process easier. I'll show you the difference between the modeling process that a top analyst uses versus the procedure of a less rigorous analyst. These tips come up again and again throughout this book!

Tip 1: Conduct A Lot of Research Before Starting

Before you begin the regression analysis, you should review the literature to develop an understanding of the relevant variables, their relationships, and the expected coefficient signs and effect magnitudes. Developing your knowledge base helps you gather the correct data in the first place, and it allows you to specify the best regression equation without resorting to data mining.

Regrettably, large data bases stuffed with handy data combined with automated model building procedures have pushed analysts away from this knowledge-based approach. Data mining procedures can build a misleading model that has significant variables and a good R-squared using randomly generated data!

The output represents a model that stepwise regression built from entirely random data. In the final step, the R-squared is decently high, and all of the variables have very low p-values!

	----Step 1----		----Step 2----		----Step 3----	
	Coef	P	Coef	P	Coef	P
Constant	0.259		0.386		0.479	
C35	-0.520	0.001	-0.531	0.000	-0.571	0.000
C28			0.379	0.012	0.418	0.002
C87					0.373	0.005
S		0.818091		0.740015		0.644120
R-sq		32.90%		47.06%		61.38%
R-sq(adj)		30.51%		43.14%		56.92%
R-sq(pred)		21.70%		33.88%		49.13%
Mallows' Cp		19.17		11.64		4.00

Automated model building procedures can have a place in the exploratory phase. However, you can't expect them to produce the correct model precisely.

Tip 2: Use a Simple Model When Possible

It seems that complex problems should require complicated regression equations. However, studies show that simplification usually produces more precise models. How simple should the models be? In many cases, three independent variables are sufficient for complex problems. (Zellner, Keuzenkamp, & McAleer, 2009)

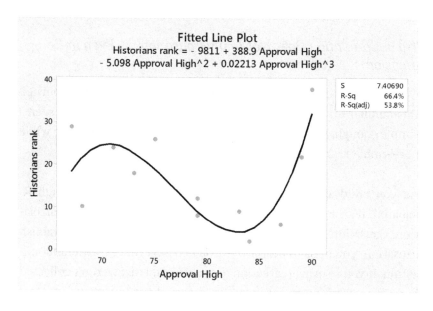

Fitted Line Plot
Historians rank = - 9811 + 388.9 Approval High
- 5.098 Approval High^2 + 0.02213 Approval High^3

S	7.40690
R-Sq	66.4%
R-Sq(adj)	53.8%

This model is too complex for the data as we saw in the section about predicted R-squared.

The tip is to start with a simple a model and then make it more complicated only when it is truly needed. If you make a model more complex, confirm that the confidence intervals for the coefficients and the prediction intervals are more precise (narrower). When you have several models with comparable predictive abilities, choose the simplest because it is likely to be the best model. Another benefit is that simpler models are easier to understand and explain to others!

As you make a model more elaborate, the R-squared increases, but it becomes more likely that you are customizing it to fit the vagaries of your specific dataset rather than actual relationships in the population. This overfitting reduces generalizability and produces results that you can't trust.

Chapter 6 shows how both adjusted R-squared and predicted R-squared can help you include the correct number of variables and avoid overfitting.

Tip 3: Correlation Does Not Imply Causation . . . Even in Regression

Correlation does not imply causation. Statistics classes have burned this familiar mantra into the brains of all statistics students! It seems simple enough. However, analysts can forget this important rule while performing regression analysis.

As you build a model that has significant variables and a high R-squared, it's easy to forget that you might only be revealing correlation. Causation is an entirely different matter. Typically, to establish causation, you need to perform a designed experiment with randomization. If you're using regression to analyze data that weren't collected in such an experiment, you can't be certain about causation.

Fortunately, correlation can be just fine in some cases. For instance, if you want to predict the outcome, you don't always need variables that have causal relationships with the dependent variable. If you measure a variable that is related to changes in the outcome but doesn't influence the outcome, you can still obtain good predictions. Sometimes it is easier to measure these proxy variables. However, if your goal is to affect the outcome by setting the values of the input variables, you must identify variables with truly causal relationships.

For example, if vitamin consumption is only correlated with improved health but does not cause good health, then altering vitamin use won't improve your health. There must be a causal relationship between two variables for changes in one to cause changes in the other.

Tip 4: Include Graphs, Confidence, and Prediction Intervals in the Results

This tip focuses on the fact that how you present your results can influence how people interpret them. The information can be the same, but the presentation style can prompt different reactions. For instance, confidence intervals and statistical significance provide consistent information. When a p-value is less than the 0.05 significance level, the corresponding 95% confidence interval will always exclude zero. However, the impact on the reader is very different.

A study by Cumming (Cumming, 2011) finds that statistical reports which refer only to statistical significance bring about correct interpretations only 40% of the time. When the results also include confidence intervals, the percentage rises to 95%! Other research (Soyer & Hogarth, 2012) show dramatic increases in correct interpretations when you include graphs in regression analysis reports. In general, you want to make the statistical results as intuitively understandable as possible.

Tip 5: Check Your Residual Plots!

Residuals plots are a quick and easy way to check for problems in your regression model. You might not be sure whether there is a problem, but residual plots can make the answer clear! These graphs can also help you make adjustments. For instance, residual plots display patterns when you fail to model curvature that is present in your data. We covered residual plots and other assumptions in chapter 9.

Differences Between a Top Analyst and a Less Rigorous Analyst

Top analysts tend to do the following:

- Conducts research to understand the study area before starting.
- Uses large quantities of reliable data and a few independent variables with well established relationships.
- Uses sound reasoning to determine which variables to include in the regression model.
- Combines different lines of research as needed.
- Presents the results using charts, prediction intervals, and confidence intervals in a lucid manner that ensures the appropriate interpretation by others.

On the other hand, a less rigorous analyst tends to do the following:

- Does not do the research to understand the research area and similar studies.
- Uses regression outside of designed experiments to hunt for causal relationships.
- Uses data-mining to rummage for relationships because databases provide a lot of convenient data.
- Includes variables in the model based mainly on statistical significance.
- Uses a complicated model to increase R-squared.

- Reports only the basic statistics of coefficients, p-values, and R-squared values.

Identifying the Most Important Variables

You've settled on a regression model that contains independent variables that are statistically significant. By interpreting the statistical results, you can understand how changes in the independent variables are related to shifts in the dependent variable. At this point, it's natural to wonder, "Which independent variable is the most important?"

Surprisingly, determining which variable is the most important is more complicated than it first appears. For a start, you need to define what you mean by "most important." The definition should include details about your subject-area and your goals for the regression model. So, there is no one-size fits all definition for the most important independent variable. Furthermore, the methods you use to collect and measure your data can affect the seeming importance of the independent variables.

I'll help you determine which independent variable is the most important while keeping these issues in mind. First, I'll reveal surprising statistics that are not related to importance. You don't want to get tripped up by them! Then, I'll cover statistical and non-statistical approaches for identifying the most important independent variables in your regression model. I'll also include an example regression model where we'll try these methods out.

Do Not Associate Regular Regression Coefficients with the Importance of Independent Variables

The regular regression coefficients that you see in your statistical output describe the relationship between the independent variables and the dependent variable. The coefficient value represents the mean change of the dependent variable given a one-unit shift in an independent variable. Consequently, you might think you can use the absolute sizes of the coefficients to identify the most important variable.

After all, a larger coefficient signifies a greater change in the mean of the independent variable.

However, the independent variables can have dramatically different types of units, which make comparing the coefficients meaningless. For example, the meaning of a one-unit change differs considerably when your variables measure time, pressure, and temperature.

Additionally, a single type of measurement can use different units. For example, you can measure weight in grams and kilograms. If you fit two regression models using the same dataset, but use grams in one model and kilograms in the other, the weight coefficient changes by a factor of a thousand! Obviously, the importance of weight did not change at all even though the coefficient changed substantially. The model's goodness-of-fit remains the same.

Key point: Larger coefficients don't necessarily represent more important independent variables.

<u>Do Not</u> Link P-values to Importance

You can't use the coefficient to determine the importance of an independent variable, but how about the variable's p-value? Comparing p-values seems to make sense because we use them to determine which variables to include in the model. Do lower p-values represent more important variables?

Calculations for p-values include various properties of the variable, but importance is not one of them. A very small p-value does not indicate that the variable is important in a practical sense. An independent variable can have a tiny p-value when it has a very precise estimate, low variability, or a large sample size. The result is that effect sizes that are trivial in the practical sense can still have very low p-values. Consequently, when assessing statistical results, it's important to determine whether an effect size is practically significant in addition to being statistically significant.

Key point: Low p-values don't necessarily represent independent variables that are practically important.

Do Assess These Statistics to Identify Variables that might be Important

I showed how you can't use several of the more notable statistics to determine which independent variables are most important in a regression model. The good news is that there are several statistics that you can use. Unfortunately, they sometimes disagree because each one defines "most important" differently.

Standardized coefficients

As I explained previously, you can't compare the regular regression coefficients because they use different scales. However, standardized coefficients all use the same scale, which means you can compare them.

Statistical software calculates standardized regression coefficients by first standardizing the observed values of each independent variable and then fitting the model using the standardized independent variables. Standardization involves subtracting the variable's mean from each observed value and then dividing by the variable's standard deviation.

Fit the regression model using the standardized independent variables and compare the standardized coefficients. Because they all use the same scale, you can compare them directly. Standardized coefficients signify the mean change of the dependent variable given a one standard deviation shift in an independent variable.

Key point: Identify the independent variable that has the largest absolute value for its standardized coefficient.

Change in R-squared for the last variable added to the model

Many statistical software packages include a very helpful analysis. They can calculate the increase in R-squared when each variable is added to a model that already contains all of the other variables. In other words, how much does the R-squared increase for each variable when you add it to the model last?

This analysis might not sound like much, but there's more to it than is readily apparent. When an independent variable is the last one entered into the model, the associated change in R-squared represents the improvement in the goodness-of-fit that is due solely to that last variable after all of the other variables have been accounted for. In other words, it represents the *unique* portion of the goodness-of-fit that is attributable only to each independent variable.

Key point: Identify the independent variable that produces the largest R-squared increase when it is the last variable added to the model.

Example of Identifying the Most Important Independent Variables in a Regression Model

The example output shows a regression model that has three independent variables. Use this CSV data file: ImportantVariables.

The statistical output displays the coded coefficients, which are the standardized coefficients. Temperature has the standardized coefficient with the largest absolute value. This measure suggests that Temperature is the most important independent variable in the regression model.

```
Coded Coefficients

Term           Coef  SE Coef  T-Value  P-Value   VIF
Constant     249.64     1.60   156.36    0.000
Time           3.01     1.72     1.75    0.092  1.12
Pressure       9.85     1.78     5.52    0.000  1.21
Temperature  -21.92     1.70   -12.92    0.000  1.09
```

The graphical output below shows the incremental impact of each independent variable. This graph displays the increase in R-squared associated with each variable when it is added to the model last. Temperature uniquely accounts for the largest proportion of the variance. For our example, both statistics suggest that Temperature is the most important variable in the regression model.

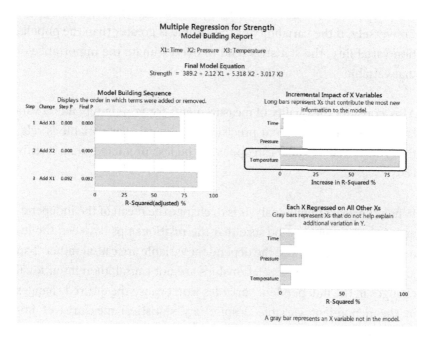

Cautions for Using Statistics to Pinpoint Important Variables

Standardized coefficients and the change in R-squared when a variable is added to the model last can both help identify the more important independent variables in a regression model—from a purely statistical standpoint. Unfortunately, these statistics can't determine the practical importance of the variables. For that, you'll need to use your knowledge of the subject area.

The manner in which you obtain and measure your sample can bias these statistics and throw off your assessment of importance.

When you collect a random sample, you can expect the sample variability of the independent variable values to reflect the variability in the population. Consequently, the change in R-squared values and standardized coefficients should reflect the correct population values.

However, if the sample contains a restricted range (less variability) for a variable, both statistics tend to underestimate the importance. Conversely, if the variability of the sample is greater than the population variability, the statistics tend to overestimate the importance of that variable.

Also, consider the quality of measurements for your independent variables. If the measurement precision for a particular variable is relatively low, that variable can appear to be less predictive than it truly is.

When the goal of your analysis is to change the mean of the independent variable, you must be sure that the relationships between the independent variables and the dependent variable are causal rather than just correlation. If these relationships are not causal, then intentional changes in the independent variables won't cause the desired changes in the dependent variable despite any statistical measures of importance.

Typically, you need to perform a randomized experiment to determine whether the relationships are causal.

Non-Statistical Issues that Help Find Important Variables

The definition of "most important" should depend on your goals and the subject-area. Practical issues can influence which variable you consider to be the most important.

For instance, when you want to affect the value of the dependent variable by changing the independent variables, use your knowledge to identify the variables that are easiest to change. Some variables can be difficult, expensive, or even impossible to change.

"Most important" is a subjective, context sensitive quality. Statistics can highlight candidate variables, but you still need to apply your subject-area expertise.

Comparing Regression Lines with Hypothesis Tests

How do you compare regression lines statistically? Imagine you are studying the relationship between height and weight and want to determine whether this relationship differs between basketball players and non-basketball players. You can graph the two regression lines to see if they look different. However, you should perform hypothesis tests to determine whether the visible differences are statistically significant.

In this section, I show you how to determine whether the differences between coefficients and constants in different regression models are statistically significant. It's very easy to do and utilizes concepts we covered earlier in this book—indicator variables and interaction effects!

Suppose we estimate the relationship between X and Y under two different conditions, processes, contexts, or other qualitative change. We want to determine whether the difference affects the relationship between X and Y. Fortunately, these statistical tests are easy to perform.

For the regression examples in this section, I use an input variable and an output variable for a fictional process. Our goal is to determine whether the relationship between these two variables changes between two conditions. First, I'll show you how to determine whether the constants are different. Then, we'll assess whether the coefficients are different.

Hypothesis Tests for Comparing Regression Constants

When the constant (y intercept) differs between regression equations, the regression lines are shifted up or down on the y-axis. The scatterplot shows how the output for Condition B is consistently higher than Condition A for any given Input. These two models have different constants. We'll use a hypothesis test to determine whether this vertical shift is statistically significant.

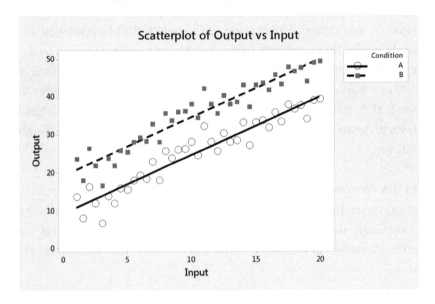

To test the difference between the constants, we need to combine the two datasets into one. Then, create a categorical variable that identifies the condition for each observation. Our combined dataset contains the three variables of Input, Condition, and Output. All we need to do now is to fit the model!

I fit the model with Input and Condition as the independent variables and Output as the dependent variable. Use the CSV data file for this example: TestConstants.

Interpreting the Results

The regression equation table displays the two constants, which differ by 10 units. We will determine whether this difference is statistically significant.

```
Regression Equation

Condition
A              Output = 9.099 + 1.5359 Input

B              Output = 19.099 + 1.5359 Input
```

Next, check the coefficients table in the statistical output.

```
Coefficients

Term           Coef   SE Coef   T-Value   P-Value   VIF
Constant       9.099    0.715     12.73     0.000
Input         1.5359   0.0542     28.32     0.000   1.00
Condition
  B           10.000    0.610     16.38     0.000   1.00
```

For Input, the p-value for the coefficient is 0.000. This value indicates that the relationship between the two variables is statistically significant. The positive coefficient indicates that as Input increases, so does Output, which matches the scatterplot.

To perform a hypothesis test on the difference between the constants, we need to assess the Condition variable. The Condition coefficient is 10, which is the vertical difference between the two models. The p-value for Condition is 0.000. This value indicates that the difference between the two constants is statistically significant. In other words, the sample evidence is strong enough to reject the null hypothesis that the population difference equals zero (i.e., no difference).

The hypothesis test supports the conclusion that the constants are different. The vertical shift is statistically significant.

Hypothesis Tests for Comparing Regression Coefficients

Let's move on to testing the difference between regression coefficients. When the coefficients are different, a one-unit change in an independent variable is related to varying changes in the mean of the dependent variable.

The scatterplot displays two Input/Output models. It appears that Condition B has a steeper line than Condition A. Our goal is to determine whether the difference between these slopes is statistically significant. In other words, does Condition affect the relationship between Input and Output?

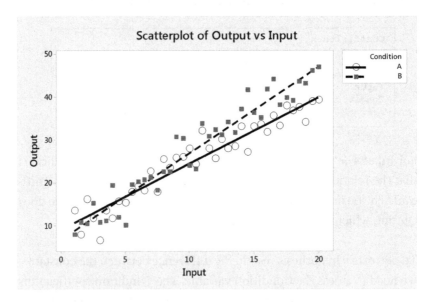

Performing this hypothesis test might seem complex, but it is straightforward. To start, we'll use the same approach for testing the constants. We need to combine both datasets into one and create a categorical Condition variable. Here is the CSV data file for this example: TestSlopes.

We need to determine whether the relationship between Input and Output depends on Condition. In statistics, when the relationship between two variables depends on another variable, it is called an interaction effect. Consequently, to perform a hypothesis test on the difference between regression coefficients, we just need to include the proper interaction term in the model! In this case, we'll include the interaction term for Input*Condition.

I fit the regression model with Input (continuous main effect), Condition (categorical main effect), and Input *Condition (interaction effect). This model produces the following results.

Interpreting the Results

```
Coefficients

Term             Coef   SE Coef  T-Value  P-Value   VIF
Constant        9.099     0.980     9.29    0.000
Input          1.5359    0.0823    18.67    0.000  2.00
Condition
   B            -2.36      1.39    -1.70    0.093  4.48
Input*Condition
   B            0.469     0.116     4.03    0.000  5.48
```

The p-value for Input is 0.000, which indicates that the relationship between Input and Output is statistically significant.

Next, look at Condition. This term is the main effect that tests for the difference between the constants. The coefficient indicates that the difference between the constants is -2.36, but the p-value is only 0.093. The lack of statistical significance indicates that we can't conclude the constants are different. However, we'll leave it in the model because it is part of the interaction term.

Now, let's move on to the interaction term (Input*Condition). The coefficient of 0.469 represents the difference between the slope coefficients for Condition A and Condition B. The p-value of 0.000 indicates that this difference is statistically significant. We can reject the null hypothesis that the difference between slopes is zero. In other words, we can conclude that Condition affects the slope of the relationship between Input and Output.

The regression equation table displays both models. Thanks to the hypothesis tests that we performed, we know that the constants are not significantly different, but the difference between the two Input coefficients is statistically significant.

```
Regression Equation

Condition
A          Output = 9.099 + 1.5359 Input

B          Output = 6.740 + 2.0050 Input
```

By including a categorical variable in regression models, it's simple to perform hypothesis tests to determine whether the differences between constants and coefficients are statistically significant. These tests are beneficial when you can see differences between models and you want to support your observations with p-values.

How High Does R-squared Need to Be?

How high does R-squared need to be in regression analysis? That seems to be an eternal question.

Previously, I explained how to interpret R-squared. I showed how the interpretation of R^2 is not always straightforward. A low R-squared isn't always a problem, and a high R-squared doesn't automatically indicate that you have a good model.

So, how high should R-squared be? The definitive answer is . . . it depends. You'll need some patience because my assertion is that this question is the wrong question. In this section, I reveal why it is the wrong question and which questions you should ask instead.

How High Does R-squared Need to be is the Wrong Question

How high does R-squared need to be? If you think about it, there is only one correct answer. R-squared should accurately reflect the percentage of the dependent variable variation that the linear model explains. Your R^2 should not be any higher or lower than this value.

The correct R^2 value depends on your study area. Different research questions have different amounts of variability that are inherently unexplainable. Case in point, humans are hard to predict. Any study that attempts to predict human behavior will tend to have R-squared values less than 50%. However, if you analyze a physical process and have very good measurements, you might expect R-squared values over 90%. There is no one-size fits all best answer for how high R-squared should be.

Consequently, the answer to "how high does R-squared need to be?" is that it depends on the amount of variability that is actually explainable. Clearly, your R-squared should not be greater than the amount of variability that is actually explainable—which can happen in regression. To see if your R-squared is in the right ballpark, compare your R^2 to those from other studies.

Chasing a high R^2 value can produce an inflated value and a misleading model. Adjusted R-squared and predicted R-squared can help you avoid these problems.

Define Your Objectives for the Regression Model

When you wonder if the R-squared is high enough, it's probably because you want to know if the regression model satisfies your objectives. Given your requirements, does the model meet your needs? Therefore, you need to define your objectives before proceeding.

To determine whether a model meets your objectives, you'll need to ask different questions because R^2 doesn't address this issue. The correct questions depend on which of the following is your primary purpose for the model:

- Explanatory Model: Your goal is to understand the relationships between the independent variables and dependent variable.
- Predictive Model: Your goal is to obtain useful predictions for the dependent variable.

R-squared and Understanding the Relationships between the Variables

If your primary goal is to understand the relationships between the variables in your model, the answer to how high R-squared needs to be is very simple. For this objective, R^2 is irrelevant.

This statement might surprise you. However, the interpretation of the significant relationships in a regression model does not change regardless of whether your R^2 is 15% or 85%! The regression coefficients define the relationship between each independent variable and the dependent variable. The interpretation of the coefficients doesn't change based on the value of R-squared.

Suppose we have a statistically significant coefficient that equals 2. This coefficient indicates that the mean of the dependent variable increases by 2 for every one-unit increase in the independent variable *irrespective* of the R^2 value.

The question about how high R-squared needs to be doesn't make sense in this context because it *doesn't matter*. A small R^2 doesn't nullify or change the interpretation of the coefficient for an independent variable that is statistically significant. I'll show how this works in more detail later in this chapter.

Instead of wondering if your R-squared value is high enough, you should ask the following questions to ensure that you can trust your results:

- Do I have a sound basis for my model?
- Can I trust my data?
- Do the residual plots look good?
- Do the results fit theory?
- How do I interpret the regression coefficients and P-values?

R-squared and Predicting the Dependent Variable

On the other hand, if your primary goal is to use your regression model to predict the value of the dependent variable, R-squared is a consideration.

Predictions are more complex than just the single predicted value. Predictions include a margin of error. More precise predictions have a smaller amount of error.

R^2 is relevant in this context because it is a measure of the error. Lower R^2 values correspond to models with more error, which in turn produces predictions that are less precise. In other words, if your R^2 is too low, your predictions will be too imprecise to be useful.
A low R-squared can be an indicator of imprecision predictions. However, R^2 doesn't tell you directly whether the predictions are sufficiently precise for your requirements.

We need a direct measure of precision that uses the units of the dependent variable. That's why asking, "How high does R-squared need to be?" still is not the correct question.

Instead, you should ask the previous questions plus the following question:

- Are the prediction intervals precise enough for my requirements?

Using Prediction intervals to Assess Precision

Most statistical software can calculate prediction intervals, and they are easy to use.

A prediction interval is a range where a single new observation is likely to fall given values of the independent variable(s) that you specify. These ranges incorporate the margin of error around the predicted value. If the prediction intervals are too wide, the predictions don't provide useful information. Narrow prediction intervals represent more precise predictions. The fitted line displays the prediction intervals graphically.

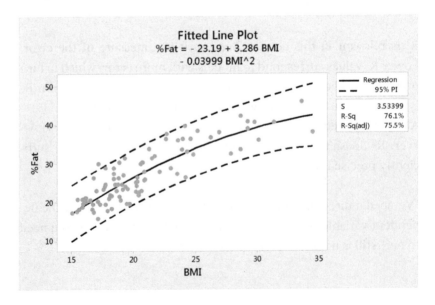

In chapter 10, where I discuss using regression analysis to make predictions, I present the model displayed in the graph. This model uses

BMI to predict the percentage of body fat. The 95% prediction interval for a BMI of 18 is 16-30% body fat. We can be 95% confident that an individual with a BMI of 18 will fall within this range.

At this point, you need to use client requirements, spec limits, and subject area knowledge to determine whether the prediction intervals are narrow enough to represent meaningful predictions. By assessing the prediction intervals, you are evaluating the precision of the model directly rather than relying on an arbitrary cut-off value for R-squared.

R-squared Is Overrated!

Asking "How high does R-squared need to be?" is usually not the correct question to ask. You probably want to know if the regression model can meet your needs. To this end, there are better questions that you should ask.

R-squared gets all of the attention for assessing the goodness-of-fit. It seems like a simple statistic to interpret. However, evaluating the fit involves more than just this single statistic. You need to use subject area knowledge, residual plots, coefficients, and prediction intervals if you're making predictions.

However, R-squared does have some good uses. For one thing, compare your R^2 value to values from similar studies. If your R^2 is markedly higher or lower, you should investigate because there might be a problem.

Don't forget about the standard error of the regression (S), which is a different type of goodness-of-fit measure that is more useful when you need to make predictions.

Five Reasons Why R-squared can be Too High

When your regression model has a high R-squared, you assume it's a good thing. You want a high R-squared, right? However, as I'll show you, a high R-squared can occasionally indicate that your model has a problem. I'll explain five reasons why your R-squared can be too high and how to determine whether one of them affects your regression model.

The five reasons I go over aren't a complete list, but they are the most common explanations.

High R-squared Values can be a Problem

S	119.674
R-Sq	Wow! 95.8%
R-Sq(adj)	95.5%

Let's start by defining how R-squared can be too high.

R-squared is the percentage of the dependent variable variation that the model explains. The value in your statistical output is an estimate of the population value that is based on your sample. Like other estimates in inferential statistics, you want your R-squared estimate to be close to the population value.

The issues I'm discussing can create situations where the R^2 in your output is much higher than the correct value for the entire population. Additionally, these conditions can cause other problems, such as misleading coefficients. Consequently, it *is* possible to have an R-squared value that is too high even though that sounds counter-intuitive.

High R^2 values are not always a problem. In fact, sometimes you can legitimately expect very large values. For example, if you are studying a physical process and have very precise and accurate measurements, it's possible to obtain valid R-squared values in the high 90s.

On the other hand, human behavior inherently has much more unexplainable variability, and this produces R^2 values that are usually less than 50%. 90% is way too high in this context!

You need to use your knowledge of the subject area to determine what R^2 values are reasonable. Compare your study to comparable studies to see what values they obtained. How inherently unpredictable is your research question?

If your R-squared value is too high, consider the following potential explanations. To determine whether any apply to your regression model, use your expertise, knowledge about your sample data, and the details about the process you used to fit the model.

Reason 1: R-squared is a biased estimate

Here's a potential surprise for you. The R-squared value in your regression output has a tendency to be too high. When calculated from a sample, R^2 is a biased estimator. In statistics, a biased estimator is one that is systematically higher or lower than the population value. R-squared estimates tend to be greater than the correct population value. This bias causes some researchers to avoid R^2 altogether and use adjusted R^2 instead.

Think of R-squared as a defective bathroom scale that reads too high on average. That's the last thing you want! Statisticians have long understood that linear regression methodology gets tripped up by chance correlations that are present in the sample, which causes an inflated R^2.

If you had a bathroom scale that reads too high, you'd adjust it downward so that it displays the correct weight on average. Adjusted R-squared does just that with the R^2 value. Adjusted R-squared reduces the value of R-squared until it becomes an unbiased estimate of the population value. Statisticians refer to this as R-squared shrinkage.

To determine the correct amount of shrinkage, the calculations compare the sample size to the number of terms in the model. When there are few samples per term, the R^2 bias tends to be larger and requires more shrinkage to correct. Conversely, models with many samples per term need less shrinkage.

The graph displays the amount of shrinkage required based on the number of samples per term.

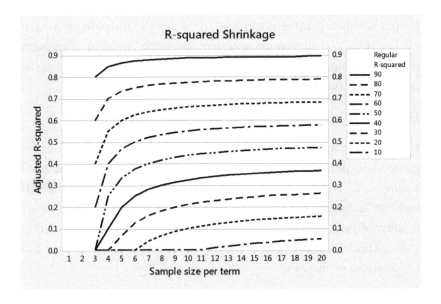

I've also written about using adjusted R-squared in a different context. Adjusted R-squared allows you to compare the goodness-of-fit for models with different numbers of terms.

Reason 2: Overfitting your model

Overfitting a model is a condition where a statistical model begins to describe the random error in the data rather than the relationships between variables. This problem occurs when the model is too complex. Unfortunately, one of the symptoms of an overfit model is an R-squared value that is too high.

While the R^2 looks good, there can be serious problems with an overfit model. For one thing, the regression coefficients represent the noise rather than the genuine relationships in the population. Additionally, an overfit regression model is tailor-made to fit the random quirks of one sample and is unlikely to fit the random quirks of another sample. Thus, overfitting a regression model reduces its generalizability outside the original dataset.

Adjusted R-squared isn't designed to detect overfitting, but predicted R-squared can.

Reason 3: Data mining and chance correlations

Data mining is the process of fitting many different models, trying many different independent variables, and primarily using statistical significance to build the final model rather than being guided by theory. This process introduces a variety of problems, including misleading coefficients and an inflated R-squared value.

For all hypothesis tests, including tests for regression coefficients, there is always the chance of rejecting a null hypothesis that is actually true (Type I error). This error rate equals your significance level, which is often 5%.

Let's apply this to regression analysis. When you fit many models, you are performing many hypothesis tests on all of the coefficients. In fact, if you use an automated model building procedure like stepwise or best subsets regression, you might be performing hundreds if not thousands of hypothesis tests on your sample. With many tests, you will inevitably encounter false positives. If you are guided mainly by statistical significance, you'll keep these variables in the model.

How serious is this problem? In chapter 8, you saw how data mining can produce statistically significant variables and a high R^2 from data that are randomly generated!

The answer lies in conducting subject-area research before you begin your study. This research helps you reduce the number of models you fit and allows you to compare your results to theory.

Reason 4: Trends in Panel (Time Series) Data

If you have panel data and your dependent variable and an independent variable both have trends over time, this can produce inflated R-squared values. Try a time series analysis or include time-related independent variables in your regression model. For instance, try lagging and differencing your variables.

Reason 5: Form of a Variable

If you include a different form of the same variable for both the dependent variable and an independent variable, you obtain an artificially inflated R-squared.

For example, if the dependent variable is temperature in Celsius and your model contains an independent variable of temperature on a different scale, your R^2 is nearly 100%. That's an obvious example, but there are more subtle forms of it. For instance, you can expect an inflated R^2 value if your dependent variable is poverty rate and one of your independent variables is income. Poverty rate is defined by income.

Models with Significant Variables but a Low R^2

Low R-squared values for regression models can seem like a problem, but that might not be the case.

If your regression model contains independent variables that are statistically significant, you might expect to have a reasonably high R-squared value. This combination of significant variables and a high R-squared makes sense.

In this situation, changes in the significant independent variables are correlated with shifts in the dependent variable. Correspondingly, the high R-squared value signifies that your model explains a good proportion of the variability in the dependent variable.

That seems logical, right?

But what if your model has independent variables that are statistically significant but it has a *low* R-squared value? This combination indicates that the independent variables are correlated with the dependent variable, but they do not explain much of the variability in the dependent variable.

Over the years, I've had many questions about how to interpret this combination. Some people have wondered whether the significant variables are meaningful. Do these results even make sense? Yes, they do!

In this section, I show how to interpret a model that has significant independent variables but a low R-squared. To do this, I'll compare regression models with low and high R-squared values so you can really grasp the similarities and differences and what it all means.

Comparing Regression Models with Low and High R-squared Values

Like many concepts in statistics, it's so much easier to understand this one using graphs. In fact, research finds that charts are crucial to convey certain information about regression models accurately.

Consequently, I'll use fitted line plots to illustrate the concepts for models with one independent variable. However, these interpretations remain valid for multiple regression.

Let's consider two regression models that assess the relationship between Input and Output. In both models, Input is statistically significant. The equations for these models are below:

- Output1 = 44.53 + 2.024*Input
- Output2 = 44.86 + 2.134*Input

These two regression equations are almost exactly equal. If you saw only the equations, you'd think the models are very similar. Now consider that the R-squared for the Output1 model is 14.7% and for Output2 it is 86.5%. The models aren't as similar as they first appear.

Graphs can really bring the differences to life. Let's see what these models and data actually look like. In the two graphs below, I made the scales the same to allow for valid comparisons. For this example, use the CSV data file: HighLowRsquaredData.

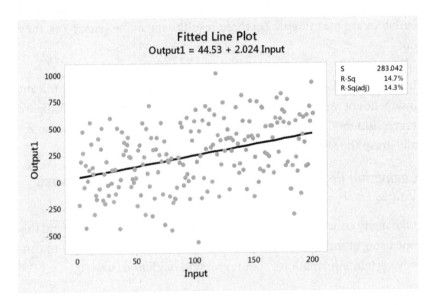

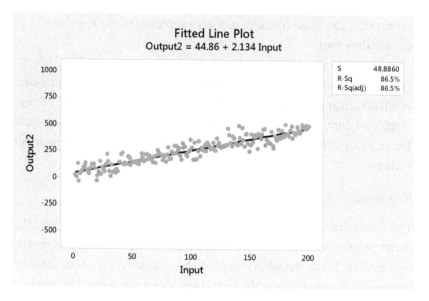

Fitted Line Plot
Output2 = 44.86 + 2.134 Input

S	48.8860
R-Sq	86.5%
R-Sq(adj)	86.5%

Whoa! Did you expect that much of a difference?

To understand how to interpret a regression model with significant independent variables but a low R-squared, we'll compare the similarities and the differences between these two models.

Regression Model Similarities

The models are similar in the following ways:

- The equations are nearly equal: Output = 44 + 2 * Input
- Input is significant with a p-value < 0.001

Additionally, the regression lines in both plots provide an unbiased fit to the upward trend in both datasets. They have the same upward slope of 2.

Interpreting a regression coefficient that is statistically significant does not change based on the R-squared value. Both graphs show that if you move to the right on the x-axis by one unit of Input, Output increases on the y-axis by an average of two units. This mean change

301

in output is the same for both models even though the R-squared values are different.

Furthermore, if you enter the same Input value in the two equations, you'll obtain approximately equal predicted values for Output. For example, an Input of 10 produces predicted values of 66.2 and 64.8. These values represent the predicted *mean* value of the dependent variable.

Regression Model Differences

The similarities all focus around the mean—the mean change and the mean predicted value. However, the biggest difference between the two models is the *variability* around those means. I'd guess that the difference in variability is the first thing about the plots that grabbed your attention.

While the regression coefficients and predicted values focus on the mean, R-squared measures the scatter of the data around the regression lines. That's why the two R-squared values are so different. For a given dataset, higher variability around the regression line produces a lower R-squared value.

Take a look at the chart with the low R-squared. Even these relatively noisy data have a significant trend. You can see that as the Input value increases, the Output value also increases. This statistically significant relationship between the variables tells us that knowing the value of Input provides information about the value of Output. The difference between the models is the spread of the data points around the predicted mean at any given location along the regression line.

Be sure to keep the low R-squared graph in mind if you need to comprehend a model that has significant independent variables but a low R-squared!

While the two models produce mean predictions that are almost the same, the variability (i.e., the precision) around the predictions is different. I'll show you how to assess precision using prediction intervals. This method is particularly useful when you have more than one independent variable and can't graph the models to see the spread of data around the regression line.

Using Prediction Intervals to See the Variability

A prediction interval is a range where a single new observation is likely to fall given values of the independent variables that you specify. Narrower prediction intervals represent more precise predictions.

The following statistical output displays the fitted values and prediction intervals that are associated with an Input value of 10 for both models. The first output is for the model with the low R-squared.

```
Prediction for Output1

Regression Equation

Output1 = 44.5 + 2.024 Input


Variable Setting
Input        10


   Fit     SE Fit        95% CI               95% PI
64.7766   37.2129   (-8.60793, 138.161)  (-498.190, 627.743)
```

```
Prediction for Output2

Regression Equation

Output2 = 44.86 + 2.1343 Input


Variable Setting
Input        10


   Fit     SE Fit        95% CI               95% PI
66.2076   6.42728   (53.5329, 78.8823)  (-31.0260, 163.441)
```

As I mentioned earlier, the mean predicted values (i.e., the fit) are nearly equal. However, the prediction intervals are very different because they incorporate the variability. The high variability/low R-squared model has a prediction interval of approximately -500 to 630. That's over 1100 units!

On the other hand, the low variability/high R-squared model has a much narrower prediction interval of roughly -30 to 160, about 190 units.

After seeing the variability in the data, the differing levels of precision should make sense.

Key Points about Low R-squared Values

Let's go over the key points.

- Regression coefficients and fitted values represent means.
- R-squared and prediction intervals represent variability.
- You interpret the coefficients for significant variables the same way regardless of the R-squared value.
- Low R-squared values can warn of imprecise predictions.

What can be done about that low R-squared value? That's the next question I usually hear in this context. Often, the first thought is to add more variables to the model to increase R-squared.

If you can find legitimate predictors, that can work in some cases. However, for every study area there is an inherent amount of unexplainable variability. For instance, studies that attempt to predict human behavior generally have R-squared values less than 50%. People are hard to predict. You can force a regression model to go past this point but it comes at the cost of misleading regression coefficients, p-values, and R-squared.

Adjusted R-squared and predicted R-squared are tools that help you avoid this problem.

If you are mainly interested in understanding the relationships between the variables, the good news is that a low R-squared does not negate the importance of any significant variables. Even with a low R-squared, statistically significant P-values continue to identify relationships and coefficients have the same interpretation. Generally, you have no additional cause to discount these findings.

CHAPTER 12

Choosing the Correct
Type of Regression

Throughout this book, I've focused on using ordinary least squares linear regression. Analysts use this type most frequently and it will serve you well. However, there are numerous other types of regression models that you can use. This choice often depends on the kind of data you have for the dependent variable and the type of model that provides the best fit. In this chapter, I cover other types of regression analyses and how to decide which one is right for your data.

I'll provide an overview along with information to help you choose. I organize the types of regression by the different kinds of dependent variable. If you're not sure which procedure to use, determine which type of dependent variable you have, and then focus on that section. This process should help narrow the choices! I'll cover regression models that are appropriate for dependent variables that measure continuous, categorical, and count data.

While these types of regression are beyond the scope of this book, I hope this information points you in the right direction if you need to use a different type of analysis.

Continuous Dependent Variables

Regression analysis with a continuous dependent variable is probably the first type that comes to mind. While this is the primary case, you still need to decide which one to use.

Continuous variables are a measurement on a continuous scale, such as weight, time, and length.

Linear regression

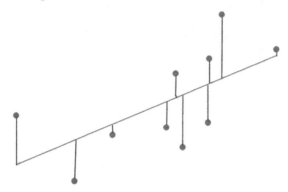

OLS produces the fitted line that minimizes the sum of the squared differences between the data points and the line.

Linear regression, also known as ordinary least squares (OLS) and linear least squares, is the real workhorse of the regression world. Use linear regression to understand the mean change in a dependent variable given a one-unit change in each independent variable. You can also use polynomials to model curvature and include interaction effects. Despite the term "linear model," this type can model curvature.

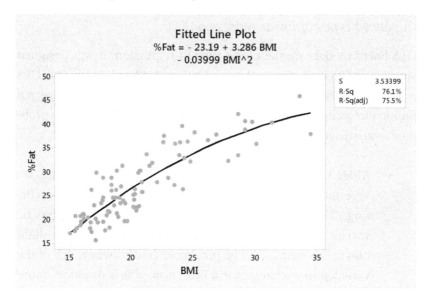

Linear model that uses a polynomial to model curvature.

This analysis estimates parameters by minimizing the sum of the squared errors (SSE). Linear models are the most common and most straightforward to use. If you have a continuous dependent variable, linear regression is probably the first type you should consider.

There are some special options available for linear regression.

Fitted line plots: If you have one independent variable and the dependent variable, use a fitted line plot to display the data along with the fitted regression line and essential regression output. These graphs make understanding the model more intuitive.

Stepwise regression and Best subsets regression: These automated methods can help identify candidate variables early in the model specification process.

Advanced types of linear regression

OLS linear models are the oldest type of regression. It was designed so that statisticians can do the calculations by hand. However, OLS has several weaknesses, including a sensitivity to both outliers and multicollinearity, and it is prone to overfitting. To address these problems, statisticians have developed several advanced variants:

- **Ridge regression** allows you to analyze data even when severe multicollinearity is present and helps prevent overfitting. This type of model reduces the large, problematic variance that multicollinearity causes by introducing a slight bias in the estimates. The procedure trades away much of the variance in exchange for a little bias, which produces more useful coefficient estimates when multicollinearity is present.
- **Lasso regression** (least absolute shrinkage and selection operator) performs variable selection that aims to increase prediction accuracy by identifying a simpler model. It is similar to Ridge regression but with variable selection.
- **Partial least squares (PLS)** regression is useful when you have very few observations compared to the number of independent variables or when your independent variables are highly correlated. PLS decreases the independent variables down to a smaller number of uncorrelated components, similar to Principal Components Analysis. Then, the procedure performs linear regression on these components rather than the original data. PLS emphasizes developing predictive models and is not used for screening variables. Unlike OLS, you can include multiple continuous dependent variables. PLS uses the correlation structure to identify smaller effects and model multivariate patterns in the dependent variables.

Nonlinear regression

Nonlinear regression also requires a continuous dependent variable, but it provides a greater flexibility to fit curves than linear regression.

Like OLS, nonlinear regression estimates the parameters by minimizing the SSE. However, nonlinear models use an iterative algorithm rather than the linear approach of solving them directly with matrix equations. What this means for you is that you need to worry about which algorithm to use, specifying good starting values, and the possibility of either not converging on a solution or converging on a local minimum rather than a global minimum SSE. And, that's in addition to specifying the correct functional form!

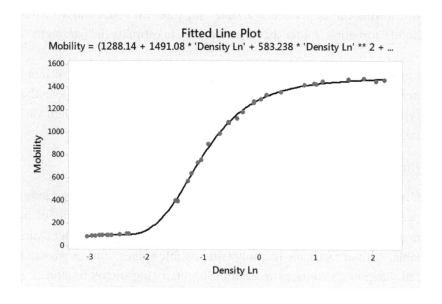

Fitted Line Plot
Mobility = (1288.14 + 1491.08 * 'Density Ln' + 583.238 * 'Density Ln' ** 2 + ...

Nonlinear model of electron mobility by density.

Most nonlinear models have one continuous independent variable, but it is possible to have more than one. When you have one independent variable, you can graph the results using a fitted line plot.

My advice is to fit a model using linear regression first and then determine whether the linear model provides an adequate fit by checking the residual plots. If you can't obtain a good fit using linear regression, then try a nonlinear model because it can fit a wider variety of curves.

I always recommend that you try OLS first because it is easier to perform and interpret.

Categorical Dependent Variables

So far, we've looked at models that require a continuous dependent variable. Next, let's move on to categorical independent variables. A categorical variable has values that you can put into a countable number of distinct groups based on a characteristic. Logistic regression transforms the dependent variable and then uses Maximum Likelihood Estimation, rather than least squares, to estimate the parameters.

Logistic regression describes the relationship between a set of independent variables and a categorical dependent variable. Choose the type of logistic model based on the type of categorical dependent variable you have.

Binary Logistic Regression

Use binary logistic regression to understand how changes in the independent variables are associated with changes in the probability of an event occurring. This type of model requires a binary dependent variable. A binary variable has only two possible values, such as pass and fail. Chapter 13 contains an example of binary logistic regression.

Example: Political scientists assess the odds of the incumbent U.S. President winning reelection based on stock market performance.

Ordinal Logistic Regression

Ordinal logistic regression models the relationship between a set of predictors and an ordinal response variable. An ordinal response has at least three groups which have a natural order, such as hot, medium, and cold.

Example: Market analysts want to determine which variables influence the decision to buy large, medium, or small popcorn at the movie theater.

Nominal Logistic Regression

Nominal logistic regression models the relationship between a set of independent variables and a nominal dependent variable. A nominal variable has at least three groups which do not have a natural order, such as scratch, dent, and tear.

Example: A quality analyst studies the variables that affect the odds of the type of product defects: scratches, dents, and tears.

Count Dependent Variables

If your dependent variable is a count of items, events, results, or activities, you might need to use a different type of regression model. Counts are nonnegative integers (0, 1, 2, etc.). Count data with higher means tend to be normally distributed and you can often use OLS. However, count data with smaller means can be skewed, and linear regression might have a hard time fitting these data. For these cases, there are several types of models you can use.

Poisson regression

Count data frequently follow the Poisson distribution, which makes Poisson Regression a good possibility. Poisson variables are a count of something over a constant amount of time, area, or another consistent length of observation. Counts are nonnegative integers. With a Poisson variable, you can calculate and assess a rate of occurrence. A classic example of a Poisson dataset is provided by Ladislaus Bortkiewicz, a Russian economist, who analyzed annual deaths caused by horse kicks in the Prussian Army from 1875-1984.

Use Poisson regression to model how changes in the independent variables are associated with changes in the counts. Poisson models are similar to logistic models because they use Maximum Likelihood Estimation and transform the dependent variable using the natural log. Poisson models can be suitable for rate data, where the rate is a count of events divided by a measure of that unit's *exposure* (a consistent unit of observation). For example, homicides per month.

Example: An analyst uses Poisson regression to model the number of calls that a call center receives daily.

Alternatives to Poisson regression for count data

Not all count data follow the Poisson distribution because this distribution has some stringent restrictions. Fortunately, there are alternative analyses you can perform when you have count data.

Negative binomial regression: Poisson regression assumes that the variance equals the mean. When the variance is greater than the mean, your model has overdispersion. A negative binomial model, also known as NB2, can be more appropriate when overdispersion is present.

Zero-inflated models: Your count data might have too many zeros to follow the Poisson distribution. In other words, there are more zeros than Poisson regression predicts. Zero-inflated models assume that two separate processes work together to produce the excessive zeros. One process determines whether there are zero events or more than zero events. The other is the Poisson process that determines how many events occur, some of which can be zero. An example makes this clearer!

Suppose park rangers count the number of fish caught by each park visitor as they exit the park. A zero-inflated model might be appropriate for this scenario because there are two processes for catching zero fish:

- Some park visitors catch zero fish because they did not go fishing.
- Other visitors went fishing, and some of these people caught zero fish.

As you can see, there are many different types of regression analysis. If OLS doesn't work for your data, there's undoubtedly a type of regression that will! Knowing how to use OLS is extremely helpful for using these other types of analysis.

CHAPTER 13

Examples of Other
Types of Regression

The last chapter contains examples of several different types of regression analysis to introduce you to the potential of these analyses. These regression examples include the datasets so you can try them yourself! We'll explore log-log plots and binary logistic regression, which are two of the more common alternatives to ordinary least squares regression.

Using Log-Log Plots to Determine If Size Matters

Log-log plots display data in two dimensions where both axes use logarithmic scales. When one variable changes as a constant power of another, a log-log graph shows the relationship as a straight line. In this section, I'll show you why these graphs are valuable and how to interpret them.

These plots allow us both to test whether data fits a power law relationship in the form of $Y = kX^n$ and to extract both k and n. If the data points don't follow a straight line, we know that X and Y do not have a power law relationship. Furthermore, a log-log graph displays the relationship $Y = kX^n$ as a straight line such that log k is the constant and n is the slope. Equivalently, the linear function is: log Y = log k + n log X. It's easy to see if the relationship follows a power law and to read k and n right off the graph!

In this section, I work through two example log-log plots to see whether some real-world data follow a power law relationship. It's also a fantastic illustration of the truth behind John Tukey's observation that, "The best thing about being a statistician is that you get to play in everyone's backyard." I agree enthusiastically!

I love reading and watching scientific material. These are the other backyards that Tukey mentions. My statistical knowledge often helps me to understand the subject matter better. In this case, I was watching and noticed what seemed to be an error in the "Size Matters" episode of the BBC program *Wonders of Life*. Professor Brian Cox presents a graph that displays the relationship between the mass of mammals and their metabolic rate. And this becomes one of our example log-log plots!

Does the Mass of Mammals Affect Their Metabolism?

Brian Cox is a theoretical physicist and a really smart guy. He's also one of my favorite science presenters. So, I was surprised when his explanation of a linear regression model appeared incorrect. Below is a closer look at the model he presents, and his interpretation.

Cox points to the straight line and says, "That implies, gram-for-gram, large animals use less energy than small animals . . . because the slope is less than one."

In linear regression, it doesn't matter that the slope is less than 1. Instead, the fact that the line is straight tells us that both small and large mammals follow a constant relationship. If you increase mass by 1 gram for both a small mammal and for a large mammal, metabolism rises by the same average amount for both sizes. In other words, gram-for-gram, size *doesn't* seem to matter!

However, I didn't think Cox would make such a fundamental mistake, so I investigated. I found that biologists use log-log plots to display the relationship between mammal mass and their basal metabolic rate. The relationship appears to be a straight line, but it follows a power law. In the program, Cox didn't mention that he was showing a log-log plot. That's a big difference!

Scientists use log-log plots for many phenomena that follow power laws. Systems can be complex and cover widely different scales. However, the exponent in a power law relationship remains the same at all scales of a system. You can use power laws to model the sizes of the craters on the power, word frequencies, and earthquakes.

The fact that we're looking at a log-log plot drastically changes our interpretation. In regression, you can use log-log plots to transform the data to model curvature using linear regression even when it represents a nonlinear function. Let's analyze similar mammal data ourselves and learn how to interpret the log-log plot.

Example: Log-Log Plot of Mammal Mass and Basal Metabolic Rate

We'll use the PanTHERIA database to model the relationship between mammal mass and metabolic with a log-log plot. This dataset includes 572 mammals that range from the masked shrew (4.2 grams) to the common eland (562,000 grams)—which is a much larger sample-size than Brian Cox's dataset. Here is the CSV data file so you can try both log-log plot examples for yourself: Mammals.

Most statistical software can create a log-log plot. Here's what it looks like for the mammal dataset.

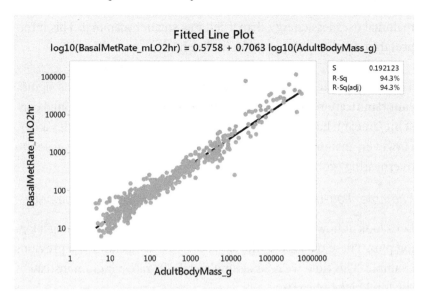

The data clearly follow a straight line, which indicates they follow a power law relationship. The p-value for the slope (0.7063) is 0.000 (not shown), indicating that it is statistically significant. The R-squared of 94.3% is impressive, particularly when you consider that different researchers collected these data in various settings and included a wide range of mammals from entirely different habits!

Using the constant and slope, we can rewrite it in the power law form:

Metabolic Rate $= 0.5758 \text{Mass}^{0.7063}$

The exponent's value is consistent with recently published estimates.

When a slope on a log-log plot is between 0 and 1, it signifies that the nonlinear effect of the dependent variable lessens as its value increases. For the mammal data, the exponent (0.7063) is in this range, which indicates that as mammals become more massive, the increase in metabolic rate slows down. In other words, gram for gram, larger mammals use less energy than smaller mammals. Or, a cell in a larger mammal uses less energy than a cell in a smaller mammal. This interpretation fits Cox's explanation in the show.

The fact that the effect of mass on metabolism decreases has significant ramifications. If the increase in metabolic rate had remained constant (linear), humans would need to consume 16,000 calories a day. However, mammals couldn't grow more massive than a goat due to overheating problems!

Example: Log-Log Plot of Basal Metabolic Rate and Longevity

Let's look at how metabolic rate and longevity are related using a log-log plot. These data are in the same dataset we used for the previous example. This time we're assessing metabolic rate per gram instead of the total metabolic rate.

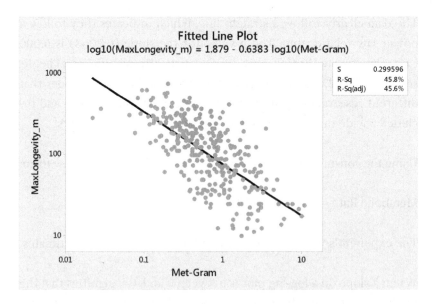

Again, the data follow a straight line, so we know that the relationship follows a power law, and it is statistically significant (p = 0.000). This time the slope is negative which indicates that as the metabolic rate per gram increases, longevity decreases. The R-squared is 45.8%, which is not bad because this factor is just one of many that can impact maximum lifespan!

We can express the relationship as a power law:

Longevity = 1.879MassPerGram $^{-0.6383}$

Like the previous log-log plot, this relationship is nonlinear. I'll graph it below using the natural scale. As the metabolic rate per gram increases, maximum longevity asymptotically approaches a minimum value of 13 months.

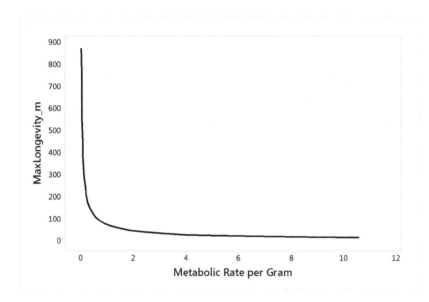

On the graph, you can see how a one-unit increase in the slow metabolic rates on the left-side of the chart produces much larger drops in longevity than a one-unit increase in the faster rates.

These two log-log plots show that size does matter for mammals. More massive mammals tend to have a slower metabolism and tend to live longer. Without a slower metabolism, we'd live only about a year!

Binary Logistic Regression: Statistical Analysis of the Republican Establishment Split

Note: I originally wrote this piece back in late 2014. I include it here to show what you can learn from binary logistic regression. Use this CSV dataset: 114congressrepublicans.

Back in 2014, House Speaker John Boehner resigned, and then Kevin McCarthy refused the position of Speaker of the House before the vote. The Republican's search for a new speaker ultimately led to Paul Ryan. Simultaneously, the Republican Freedom Caucus was making the news with a potential shutdown of the government that was controversial even amongst some Republicans.

During the Republican Presidential nomination process, there was a prominent split between candidates who were pro-establishment and anti-establishment. Of course, the end result of the dramatic 2016 U.S. Presidential election was the inauguration of a complete political outsider.

Change was in the air. Were these events related? Statistical analyses can help us identify the underlying variables. I'll use binary logistic regression to determine whether the establishment split in the Republican nomination process is also evident in the membership of the Freedom Caucus.

How Does the Freedom Caucus Fit In?

The Freedom Caucus is a faction in the U.S. House of Representatives and contains about 40 Republicans. The Freedom Caucus is also known as the "Hell No" caucus and has been known to be disruptive. Depending on your political views, these disruptions are either positive or negative events!

The Freedom Caucus tends to be described as very conservative. Based on my research, this appears to be the central property of this group. However, I'll use statistical analyses to determine whether Freedom Caucus membership is predicted by an anti-establishment outlook.

If this is verified, the disruptions caused by the Freedom Caucus and the upheaval in the Republican nomination process are linked to the common theme of an anti-establishment viewpoint. Also, I want to statistically assess whether the choice of Paul Ryan as the Speaker of the House fits this pattern.

Data for these Analyses

The House of Representatives data come from voteview.com. This website analyzes the votes by House members to determine a politician's conservativeness and establishmentarianism. I also used a Wikipedia article to determine which Republican members of the House belonged to the Freedom Caucus at that point in time.

Here's how you interpret these scores:

- Conservativeness: Higher scores represent more conservative viewpoints.
- Establishmentarianism: Higher scores represent viewpoints that favor the establishment. Lower scores represent anti-establishment viewpoints.

Graphing the House Republican Data

I'll start by graphing the data so we can see a quick picture of the situation. In the scatterplot, the points represent Republican House members by their two scores. More conservative members are further to right while those who are more against the establishment are further down. Freedom Caucus members are indicated with dark squares.

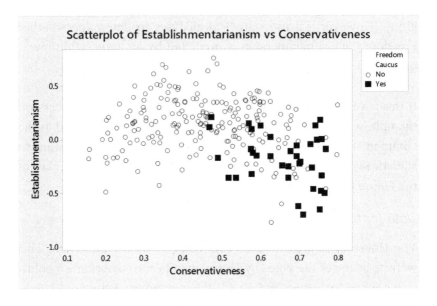

Scatterplot of Establishmentarianism vs Conservativeness

It turns out that not all politicians in the Freedom Caucus are very conservative. However, they are all at least halfway to the right on the graph. Members of the Freedom Caucus also tend to fall in the bottom half of the graph, which indicates a tendency towards anti-establishment viewpoints. It appears that both conservativeness and anti-establishment viewpoints are factors in Freedom Caucus membership.

Binary Logistic Regression Model of Freedom Caucus Membership

I'll use binary logistic regression to test these two predictors statistically. The response data are binary because Freedom Caucus membership can be only Yes or No. The table indicates that there were 36 Freedom Caucus members out of 247 House Republicans in 2015.

```
Response Information

Variable         Value   Count
Freedom Caucus   Yes       36    (Event)
                 No       211
                 Total    247
```

```
Deviance Table

Source                    DF   Adj Dev  Adj Mean  Chi-Square  P-Value
Regression                 2    77.07   38.5327       77.07    0.000
  Conservativeness         1    34.06   34.0634       34.06    0.000
  Establishmentarianism    1    14.01   14.0085       14.01    0.000
Error                    244   128.08    0.5249
Total                    246   205.14
```

This table displays the p-values for both of the predictors in our analysis. The very low p-values indicate that both predictors are statistically significant. There is sufficient evidence to conclude that changes in the predictors are related to changes in the probability of Freedom Caucus membership. In other words, both conservativeness and anti-establishment viewpoints play a role.

I did not include the interaction term because it is not statistically significant.

Unlike OLS regression, the coefficients do not have an intuitive interpretation. Instead, I'll graph them using several plots that really help you understand the results.

Graphing the Results

The table tells us that both variables are important. But we don't know the nature of the relationships between the two predictors and membership. The most intuitive way to understand these relationships is by using several graphs.

The following graphs are based on the binary logistic regression model and plot the relationships using fitted values. This is important because regression models allow you to change the values of one predictor while holding the other predictors constant. In this manner, you can isolate the role of each variable in relation to the outcome.

The contour plot shows the values of our two predictors and the corresponding fitted probabilities. The highest probabilities are in the bottom-right corner. This pattern indicates that the probability of belonging to the Freedom Caucus increases as the politician becomes more conservative and more anti-establishment.

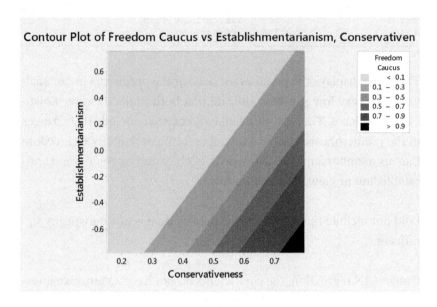

The main effects plot highlights how the regression model estimates each effect while holding the other predictor constant.

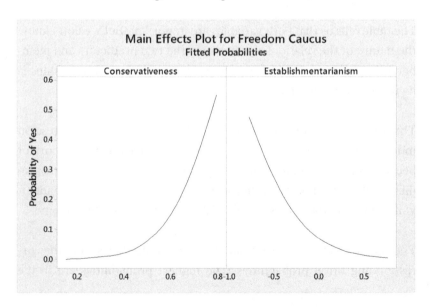

The positive relationship in the conservativeness panel shows that when politicians are more conservative (higher scores), they are more likely to belong to the Freedom Caucus. The negative relationship in the establishment panel indicates that when politicians have stronger anti-establishment opinions (lower scores), they are more likely to be Freedom Caucus members.

Freedom Caucus membership is more complex than just particularly conservative politicians. It is a combination of conservative and anti-establishment positions that predict membership.

Here's one more point to drive this home. Kevin McCarthy declined to run for Speaker and many Republicans saw Paul Ryan as a perfect candidate. Let's see how these two politicians compare by looking at their conservativeness and establishment scores. I'll standardize each variable in order to account for scale differences. Accordingly, the table displays their z-scores.

	Conservatism	Establishmentarianism
McCarthy	-0.169	0.549
Ryan	0.496	-1.180

Compared to McCarthy, Ryan is moderately more conservative but he is notably more anti-establishment. This shows which way the political winds are blowing!

Collectively, I believe these results demonstrate a multifaceted divide in a changing Republican Party. This divide helps clarify why it was hard to maintain a unified caucus, hard to choose a Speaker, and the unusual nature of the Presidential election of 2016.

My Other Books

Introduction to Statistics: An Intuitive Guide

Learn statistics without fear! Build a solid foundation in data analysis. Be confident that you understand what your data are telling you and that you can explain the results to others! I'll help you intuitively understand statistics by using simple language and deemphasizing formulas.

This guide starts with an overview of statistics and why it is so important. We proceed to essential statistical skills and knowledge about different types of data, relationships, and distributions. Then we move to using inferential statistics to expand human knowledge, how it fits into the scientific method, and how to design and critique experiments—whether it's your own or another researcher's.

Learn the fundamentals of statistics in this 255 page book:

- Why is the field of statistics vital in our data-driven society?
- Interpret graphs and summary statistics.
- Find relationships between different types of variables.
- Understand the properties of data distributions.
- Use measures of central tendency and variability.
- Interpret correlations and percentiles.
- Use probability distributions to calculate probabilities.
- Learn about the normal and binomial distributions in depth.
- Grasp the differences between descriptive and inferential statistics.
- Use data collection methodologies properly and understand sample size considerations.
- Access free downloadable datasets so you can try it yourself.

Currently available as an ebook and in print!
Learn more on my website: statisticsbyjim.com/store

Hypothesis Testing: An Intuitive Guide

Build a solid foundation for understanding how hypothesis tests work and become confident that you know when to use each type of test, how to use them properly to obtain reliable results, and interpret the results correctly. Chances are high that you'll need a working knowledge of hypothesis testing to produce new findings yourself and to understand the work of others. I present a wide variety of tests that assess characteristics of different data types. I focus on helping you grasp key concepts, methodologies, and procedures while deemphasizing equations. Learn how to use these tests painlessly!

In today's data-driven world, we hear about making decisions based on the data all the time. Hypothesis testing plays a crucial role in that process, whether you're in academia, making business decisions, or in quality improvement. Without hypothesis tests, you risk drawing the wrong conclusions and making bad decisions. The world today produces more data and more analyses designed to influence you than ever before. Are you ready for it?

In this 367-page ebook, build the skills and knowledge you'll need for effective hypothesis testing, including the following:

- Why you need hypothesis tests and how they work.
- Using significance levels, p-values, confidence intervals.
- Interpreting the results.
- Select the correct type of hypothesis test to answer your question.
- Learn how to test means, medians, variances, proportions, distributions, counts, correlations for continuous and categorical data, and outliers.
- One-Way ANOVA, Two-Way ANOVA and interaction effects.
- Estimate a good sample size for your study.
- Checking assumptions and obtaining reliable results.

- Manage the error rates for false positives and false negatives.
- Understand sampling distributions, central limit theorem, and statistical power.
- Know how t-tests, F-tests, chi-squared tests, and post hoc tests work.
- Learn about the differences between parametric, nonparametric, and bootstrapping methods.
- Examples of different types of hypothesis tests.
- Downloadable datasets so you can try it yourself.

Currently available as an ebook and in print!

Learn more on my website: statisticsbyjim.com/store

References

You can find formulas and references for the information in this book in most regression and linear model textbooks. I use the massive 1400 page *Applied Linear Statistical Models* by Neter et al. listed below. The other references apply to books and journal articles that I use to make specific points throughout this book.

Babyak, M. A. (2004). What You See May Not Be What You Get: A Brief, Nontechnical Introduction to Overfitting in Regression-Type Models. *Psychosomatic Medicine*, 411-421.

Cumming, G. (2011). *Understanding the New Statistics: Effect Sizes, Confidence Intervals, and Meta Analysis*. New York: Routledge.

Neter, J., Kutner, M. H., Nachtsheim, C. J., & Wasserman, W. (1996). Applied Linear Statistical Models 4th Edition. McGraw-Hill.

Olejnik, S., Mills, J., & Keselman, H. (2000). Using Wherry's Adjusted R2 and Mallows' Cp for Model Selection from All Possible Regressions. The Journal of Experimental Education, 365-380.

Soyer, E., & Hogarth, R. M. (2012). The illusion of predictability: How regression statistics mislead experts. International Journal of Forecasting, 695-711.

Zellner, A., Keuzenkamp, H. A., & McAleer, M. (2009). Simplicity, Inference, and Modelling: Keeping it Sophisticatedly Simple. Cambridge: Cambridge University Press.

Recommended Citation for This Book

Frost, J. (2019). Regression analysis: An intuitive guide for using and interpreting linear models. Statistics By Jim Publishing.

Index

About the Author

I'm Jim Frost, and I have extensive experience in academic research and consulting projects. In addition to my statistics website, I am a regular columnist for the American Society of Quality's *Statistics Digest*. Additionally, my most recent journal publication as a coauthor is *The Neutral Gas Properties of Extremely Isolated Early-Type Galaxies III* (2019) for the American Astronomical Society.

I've been the "data/stat guy" for research projects that range from osteoporosis prevention to analysis of online user behavior. My role has been to design the proper research settings, collect a large amount of valid measurements, and figure out what it all means. Typically, I'm the first person on the project to learn about new findings while interpreting the results of the statistical analysis. Even if the findings are not newsworthy, that thrill of discovery is an awesome job perk!

I love statistics and analyzing data! I've been performing statistical analysis on-the-job for 20 years and helping people learn statistics for over ten years at a statistical software company. I love talking and writing about statistics.

I want to help you learn statistics. But I'm not talking about learning all the equations. Don't get me wrong. Equations are necessary. Equations are the framework that makes the magic, but the truly fascinating aspects are what it all means. I want you to learn the true essence of statistics. I'll help you intuitively understand statistics by focusing on concepts and graphs. Although, there might be a few equations!

I've spent over a decade working at a major statistical software company. When you work on research projects, you generally use a regular group of statistical analyses. However, when you work at a statistical software company, you need to know of all the analyses that are in the software! I helped people use our software to gain insights and maximize the value of their own data regardless of their field.

While working at the statistical software company, I learned how to present statistics in a manner that makes statistics more intuitive. I'll be writing about my experiences and useful information about statistics. However, I'll focus on teaching the concepts in an intuitive way and deemphasize the formulas. After all, you use statistical software so you don't have to worry about the formulas and instead focus on understanding the results.

Statistics is the field of learning from data. That's amazing. It gets to the very essence of discovery. Statistics facilitates the creation of new knowledge. Bit by bit, we push back the frontier of what is known. That is what I want to teach you! My goal is to help you to see statistics through my eyes–as a key that can unlock discoveries that are in your data.

The best thing about being a statistician is that you get to play in everyone's backyard. —John Tukey

I enthusiastically agree! If you have an inquisitive mind, statistical knowledge, and data, the potential is boundless. You can play in a broad range of intriguing backyards!

That interface between a muddled reality and obtaining orderly, valid data is an exciting place. This place ties together the lofty goals of scientists to the nitty-gritty nature of the real world. It's an interaction that I've written about extensively in this book and on my blog, and I plan to continue to do so. It's where the rubber meets the road.

One of the coolest things about the statistical analysis is that it provides you with a toolkit for exploring the unknown. Christopher Columbus needed many tools to navigate to the New World and make his discoveries. Statistics are the equivalent tools for the scientific explorer because they help you navigate the sea of data that you collect.

The world is becoming a progressively data-driven place, and to draw trustworthy conclusions, you must analyze your data properly. It's surprisingly easy to make a costly mistake. Even if you're not performing your own studies, you'll undoubtedly see statistical analyses conducted by others. Can you trust their results or do they have their own agenda?

Just like there were many wrong ways for Columbus to use his tools, things can go awry with statistical analyses. I'm going to teach you how to use the tools correctly, to draw the proper conclusions, and to recognize the conclusions that should make you wary!

You'll be increasingly thankful for these tools when you see a worksheet filled with numbers and you're responsible for telling everyone what it all means.

Read more on my website: StatisticsByJim.com